LITERARY CRYPTOGRAMS

Louise B. Moll

Sterling Publishing Co., Inc.
New York

This book is dedicated to my husband, Jerry Claver, who makes my life so easy and so much fun.

My sincere thanks to the following terrific people in my life:

Dr. Jan Tobochnik, who is a whiz at writing computer programs, and who is very special to me.

Dr. Wesley E. Bramnick, for sharing his time, computer, and technical assistance with me.

Dr. Sander White, who shared his extensive library with me. (He's got great taste in books!)

My brother, Ivan Barash, and my late sister-in-law, Elaine, for promoting my books and taking a special interest in them.

Library of Congress Cataloging-in-Publication Data

Moll, Louise B.
    Literary cryptograms / by Louise B. Moll.
        p.   cm.
    Includes index.
    ISBN 0-8069-9616-1
    1. Cryptograms. I. Literary recreations. II. Title.
    GV1507.C8L656 1998
    793'.73–dc21   97-43672
                                                          CIP

10 9 8 7 6 5 4 3 2 1

Published by Sterling Publishing Company, Inc.
387 Park Avenue South, New York, N.Y. 10016
© 1998 by Louise B. Moll
Distributed in Canada by Sterling Publishing
% Canadian Manda Group, One Atlantic Avenue, Suite 105
Toronto, Ontario, Canada M6K 3E7
Distributed in Great Britain and Europe by Cassell PLC
Wellington House, 125 Strand, London WC2R 0BB, England
Distributed in Australia by Capricorn Link (Australia) Pty Ltd.
P.O. Box 6651, Baulkham Hills, Business Centre, NSW 2153, Australia
Manufactured in the United States of America
All rights reserved

Sterling ISBN 0-8069-9616-1

Contents

A Note to Cryptographers

You can't complain about not having any cryptograms to solve these days! My first four books, *The Great Book of Cryptograms*, *Clever Cryptograms*, *Baffling Cryptograms*, and *Cryptogram-A-Day Book* have produced a total of 1,546 puzzles.

I've explored philosphers, great thinkers, proverbs, and now a terrific collection of famous authors for your enjoyment. As you finish each group, you will have the flavor of who they were and how they thought. You might be surprised.

New ideas are tucked away just waiting to emerge. Hurry and get started on this book, so you'll be finished in time for the next one! You need the same supplies as before...pencils and erasers, slippers, a comfortable place to sit, and a few munchies to keep your strength up and your mind sharp.

Have fun and keep in touch!

How to Use This Book

A cryptogram is a communication in code, using a scrambled alphabet that substitutes one letter for another. Breaking it is an exercise in logic, imagination and perseverance. Logic, as you search out the patterns and structure of the words and sentences you're trying to uncover. Imagination, as you intuit words from the jumble before you. Perseverance, as you stick with the trial-and-error search.

If you've never solved a cryptogram before, you'll need to know certain facts: Each cryptogram is coded differently, but in any single quotation, the code is consistent. No letter ever stands for itself.

For example, a C could represent an E throughout the message, and an F could be an R.

WE'RE   PUZZLED   PUZZLERS
H C'F C   K Y N N A C P   K Y N N A C F X

The most common three-letter words include *the, and, but, for* and *are.* Common two-letter words are *it, is, of,* and *in.* Long word endings include *ing, ion, est* and *ied.*

Start by tracking down these telltale patterns, and with the letters you detect, you'll soon clue into other formations that will eventually reveal the message.

The order of frequency of the most used letters in the English language is:

E - T - A - O - I - N - S - H - R - D - L - U

and it has probably never helped anyone to know that!

Have fun with these crypts!

Marcus Aurelius Antoninus
(121–180)

1. T ZHHA FTJ FTUPD JH JHQDP
HYPN T ZHHA APPA, IXW RTDDPD
HJ WH TJHWMPN TD T YQJP WH
IPTN ZNTRPD TZTQJ QJ DPTDHJ.

2. HKK AZYLQD OVJU NANVLYAW
HVN JO KYTN OJVUD HLI XJUN
VJGLI YL H XYVXKN.

3. DVY DZHW OJ VSFXJG VYG
OZWWSJHHJG ISPD NKWXKY, JCHJ
WXJ WJDECJ NKCC FSZDOCJ WP
GZHW.

4. KZ KQ UNZ BSVZM ZMVZ V PVU
QMNJIB TSVY, CJZ MS QMNJIB
TSVY USLSY CSEKUUKUE ZN IKLS.

5. MZ XEW NAAFGH, JE MW XEW;
MZ XEW WKBA, NRH MW XEW.

6. VLW AEY CLR FRWQY'V SYRC CLEV VLW JYPBWKQW PQ, FRWQY'V SYRC CLWKW LW DPBWQ.

7. AOADEIA AYAZK XDI QM KQEZ UPMA XT ISQECS PI JAZA KQEZ UXTI.

8. IOT WSTHTUI MH IOT HPLT JFS PZZ; NOPI NT ZFHT FS NMU MH XQHI IOT JZBMUK LFLTUI.

9. HQSD TPVVTQ PX YQQOQO VR CJEQ J UJAAD TPIQ.

10. HXIL XD G PXKLP MN CGDDXQV LKLQHD, G PTDFXQV HMPPLQH.

11. CBJKLCS TGXUFFH UCQ RUC EKLZK KG LH CBJ XLJJGP JB GCPWVG.

12. VY VA D AODCWJXH YOVMQ
JNZ YOW ANXH YN JDVMY VM YOW
ZDUW NJ HVJW, IOVHW YOW KNBS
AYVHH FWZAWGWZA.

13. FLPI QN YPV ARD ILS LQBS
QN YPV ARD ILS YSS.

14. IZW IUHW OCUIZ CQ R XRT AD
IC FW XWRDHUWM FS IZW
CFVWLID ZW BHUDHWD.

15. MHMAQRPSDX RPCR MFSERE
SE RPM EMMV NT RPCR ZPSLP
ZSKK LNOM NYR NT SR.

Answers on page 106.

Jane Austen
(1775–1817)

1. XPNSMWNN RKE XLSMB RHMWE,
XPU CLSWMGNTSO TKLGDE WJWL
GHWN.

2. ZSR MJCYI YSHN UZN XNQKSWK
PSX QEEXSLCWA RZQU RN FCIN!

3. UFSONUTHFUU ZGUK JSVJLU
XF OCBENMFH, XFRJGUF KTFBF
NU HC TCYF CO J RGBF.

4. NA NU IBZL HNEENXPTA EGZ
AMB DZGUDBZGPU AG YB MPRYTB.

5. DUPMYC BJNHMPO JP U BGUH
ZGUW QNJWSEGX GDGNC XJNY JA
LMXEZMGA.

6. SC CSCR FOURU IPY IQ YRC, O
XIGOC NOW JRYYRL UNIX GILR
OQQRFYSIC YNOC UNR QRRDU.

7. PG PGGKMCV ML P NAFV
LAFMEKL TKLMGALL.

8. PJ PO JCHJD HFPNBCOIGGU
IERFKMGBTSBT JDIJ I OPFSGB
LIF PF VKOOBOOPKF KQ I SKKT
QKCJHFB LHOJ AB PF MIFJ KQ I
MPQB.

9. UCHUMC ZTCJFCMXCF QMZCP
FH JIBT ZTQZ ZTCPC WF
FHJCZTWEN ECY ZH GC
HGFCPXCR WE ZTCJ DHPCXCP.

10. J BJUUWY ABVWQF IJG J
CFBEFBVL CW VWBCUJVC CIF
QABE JBE GWOU CIF CFQTFU.

11. QAT XFAAQR FMLFKV ZT
MFYJSUAJ FR F HFA LURSQYR
AQL FAN RSTA VRYHZMUAJ QA
VQHTRSUAJ LURRK.

12. ONDJZ TND ID QDO
MDSEWKUQ KFZ QZXZF EUOUZI.

13. RDL XPNU RU AXL GRSNZ
VPDDRA HDZLSTAPDZ AXL
QNLPTHSLT RU AXL RAXLS.

14. L TLYO'F PALNPMLKPVM PF
ZWJO JLGPY; PK IDAGF CJVA
LYAPJLKPVM KV TVZW, CJVA TVZW
KV ALKJPAVMO PM L AVAWMK.

15. USG THS'I AHF THF NG HI
VUUE HI HSUQOGY'I, NPQ AG HRR
RMLG UPY UAS NGIQ.

Answers on pages 106–107.

Francis Bacon
(1561–1626)

1. ZHJDFX TI KUJXZ LTMMXZ, IKYXJTYXI KBXFSKYX, IXOMKY XNJTZWDTILXM.

2. JS YJWY ZQUU ALY WRRUH ASZ FSTSIQSD TMDY SNRSEY ASZ SPQUD.

3. ETCO JY Q MTTA HNOQFZQYG, HVG JG JY Q HQA YVCCON.

4. SJ WHARVGCA LV ZJYWRCREHA MJ VMRSXLSK GWJS MBA IRSMRKA-KCJGSX JO MCGMB.

5. FUZ DZXF KBOF CJ DZBQFR HX FUBF IUHAU B KHAFQOZ ABEECF ZYKOZXX.

6. PSCUFG SQ ESZG M CSYR QUDXG, TGQU WEMSX QGU.

7. DHFVWBL CG TCEL VKL XSFELV, IKLFL XSBN VCXLG, CD NHW USB GVSN S TCVVTL, VKL JFCUL ICTT DSTT.

8. HIT QXBZ XU AVWTSHZ VWT ZTNWTH, VSP ZX VWT HITKW LWKTUZ VSP UTVWZ.

9. HBP XEANAER KZ CAMYADA OSBK SA XEANAER KZ CA KEFA.

10. JPGXG CD CL PWUTL LTJWXG NGLGXTZZF UKXG KI JPG IKKZ JPTL KI JPG VCDG.

11. SC XSHX IMJCB IZZV HVJMRC PDMYVB EMXS ZLC SHLV; SC XSHX IMJCB IZZV RZDLBCY HLV CKHGTYC PDMYVB EMXS PZXS.

12. EQA KISJE JIWHEZMA HJ EI QDXA OI SADW YSHAOMJQHCJ.

13. BRHGI EBNGW KSUU EGR

TAPPQ, OSP NGGCW PVGE CFFI.

14. PHQMSPZFS QZEQYZ MOZ YPAZ

SKZ TZZN; SKZD APYY SKZHNZYWZN

PF NSPFCPFC ESKZON.

15. RQ RY W ARYPVWOJP YQWQP

CU ARGI QC BWSP UPD QBRGEY

QC IPYRVP WGI AWGN QBRGEY QC

UPWV.

Answers on page 107.

Honoré de Balzac
(1799–1850)

1. AX AF OYFAOT XK EO Y NKZOT
XWYP Y WRFEYPB, MKT XWO FYQO
TOYFKP XWYX AX AF QKTO
BAMMAIRNX XK EO JAXXD OZOTD
BYD XWYP PKJ YPB XWOP.

2. NBSSABIO DYHOQ GQAHOZ YDS
EAYO HJD WODWEO JXD
ZTBSTOEC RQDJ OBTX DHXOS.

3. PGG OHVPS RZJBF TX P
UZVRZHSI ZN WTVB PSI
RPWTBSUB.

4. OIKCMOD VI LIGKMLMNV Z
LGMNOFVCMR ZV Z ENQMNL IO
KCN RZGK IL ION LGMNOF KCZK
CN MV VYRNGMIG KI KCN IKCNG.

5. RNN XRMMQDIVV SIMIDSV FD
BFLCRPI RDS UFCJ.

6. AHFFAT KHESZ PHES
ZWFHZPWXFHQE PQI FYTHI
PTTAHEM, MQQS QI OWS, HE
AHFFAT FYHEMZ.

7. EWMK WY V PVZHKBI; NTKB WI
WY CWZIL, NK HJYI OZJYT WI;
NTKB WI WY ZVPPKC, WI HJYI OK
XVIQTKC; OJI NK FKKX WI VY
EDBP VY NK QVB.

8. UGPN LX JG JON DGKIU QIJYKN
NTIEJUZ AOIJ JON XYQ LX JG JON
NIKJO.

9. QHBVO UZ KHY OVIVCJVA MX
ZYOUTUKF DCOA HO HEYVK, MPY
MX ZYOUTUKF YOPV.

10. TQTXV JXKAKMLZ KH LM
LWYTKHW, WYURSY YT FUTHM'W
LZNLVH PMUN KW.

11. SUNYZHJWOGVGRM UN ZL WAA WOGN: UR QZHMP UM UN W CJGNGRMUVGRM, UR ZAS WOG W JGVGVXJWRYG.

12. LMBG MJ UGAVCUJ WVG IGJMAG WT PHTZ GLGAFWVMHQ.

13. H UYCCJ DT H UHEEJ ZFGDPZ CFIMFFA H EHTTDYA HAG H ZYAYZHADH.

14. QDAGE RGFFOHEF GNU SDOBU GF FBNHEYZJ GYOBGBUI MJ FAGZZ OEBUNUFBF GF MJ YNUGB HEUF.

15. SI GPAM, IPUWSIC SH BH JPIASIJSIC BH B DPGE RPGGV.

Answers on pages 107–108.

James Matthew Barrie
(1860–1937)

1. FS FI YUS SCBQ SJNS VUHNY
VNI HNTQ ACUH HNY'I CFE; IJQ
VNI CQNGGK HNTQ ACUH JFI
ABYYK EUYQ.

2. ZPC ZSAR KV PKW FRFPWJRV
VP UGSU OR FJZGU GSAR WPVRV
JM CRBRFIRW.

3. KRLRS CIJSAWR DB CK
BMMBKRKD NBDALRI NRCKRS
DQCK PBVS BTK.

4. AP AK'C RVTZVY PEO DFAQTKV,
AK'C RVFF PEO DEQXTYB.

5. A BDMF DCHDLZ OVQXI WBDW
WBF PDX HBVZF ZFTVXI
WBVQJBWZ DUF JVVI AZ HVUWB
HDWTBAXJ.

6. DFHMNDY NA BJIVVX EFBP
KDVJAA XFK EFKVC BIHMJB ZJ
CFNDY AFUJHMNDY JVAJ.

7. ZGAP ZGSZ GSHA GSW
JRYSQNA GSHA FCLDDAW LQ SQW
REZ RX GASHAQ.

8. XPDQF APD HGJLK QILQPJLF
XD XPF CJUFQ DM DXPFGQ
RBLLDX VFFO JX MGDT
XPFTQFCUFQ.

9. QV PVJVH XPFVHNLDPF KRQ
BELLBV QV PVVF EP LKEN QRHBF
XPLEB QV WPRQ LKV BRNN RA EL.

10. KYKUZ JTE HMW BN MBCM DQ
RWYKN SW SMBEL MK MTN VWEK
BS TRR MBJNKRG; TEV SMK HBGK
NJBRKN TEV RKSN BS CW TS
SMTS.

11. ZB NSJ ABMON QJ YR
YACMOOD QSI YNFJRZMWJ.

12. MZDH LN GTM SFNG
VFWWFYLZE FA GTM DLVMN, BZY
BCNF GTM EWMBGMNG KFJMW LZ
BZH CBZY.

13. WTCEQF EF YC ECZECEDT
PNRT NZ DYLECW KYECF.

14. FRGK ALYZY CLY LYEZC XV
PER CLY CZYEVWZY DY MFWRS.

15. PJDIJCA HG OCUYR UYR WJX
PUYYJA QSEQPA AJ LQ LJAB
OCUYR UYR PJDIJCAULFQ.

Answers on pages 108–109.

Ambrose Bierce
(1842–1914)

1. JMKX NE JUWXM BUNZF NE
JUWXM XMH XWUAPRH US KEQNZF
EUIHPUBT XU BU NX.

2. EZXJYEAJLQ JD LPY WLMJAG
YGOLNQJAJLQ LI EQLAUGY'D
YGDGXSMEQOG AL LPYDGMTGD.

3. GUNAZHX UL PWA PJ
USIQUWIHUPW'L SPLH RZAMUPDL
RPLLALLUPWL.

4. XHJO RPX SPZ'E RHUO QR
IHQR; EOAOWX H XQUO GFOR QX
GQAA FHIO OBBOWX.

5. NDOIK NDCRB AI ODTI
FPETOJKZ JL DKI FDCRB LERR
JKGD PIT ETOH NJGPDCG
LERRJKZ JKGD PIT PEKBH.

6. K WKNPD NW K LCKL WNPPCA,
ACHNWCL KPL CLNDCL.

7. DWVPQ DSVEX JXICUX ZCH
LYXOQ DC O IUVXPB VP PXXB.

8. QDS PNWQD MV PBV MC QDS
JBQSZBL QN QDS CNWT; MV
ZNPBV, QDS NWQTSQ NR QDS
DSBHQ.

9. MW NY SWBLMLIY LB MW NY
FLBMQAYC QM MDY MWS WO
WCY'B IWLKY.

10. D LXPG TC D HGPCXM ZFX
SDUYC ZFGM EXB ZTCF FTK SX
UTCSGM.

11. RLD NSUOXGQN MQVTQ SK
OFKGQDKK XVVMK TGRL SFKRDID
HGKASYVI FJVQ RLD OFKGQDKK
MQVTQ SK NSUOXGQN.

12. MGLJEN XT ECG IUPGH MN
PCXAC L PUDLB ACLHDT L VUSGH
LBR EGHHXYXGT L CJTMLBR.

13. OXNXSZAZIB XUI VQ APV
YZMCB: SZBQVUALMI AV
VLUBINWIB, XMC KVVC QVUALMI
AV VARIUB.

14. AGI MVZ SGJ HZVKXJJZT JG
NXQQ M OGKMS OYG YMD
OVGSPZT AGI, FIJ SGJYXSP
UGVFXTD AGI JG VZUQZRJ JYMJ
DYZ XD PVGOXSP GQTZV ZWZVA
KXSIJZ.

15. CA RDS NDSHM KT VJJDSQBTM
EWTVB KR RDSW
JDQBTUODWVWCTY, KT QDB BDD
USJP EWTVBTW BPVQ BPTR.

Answers on page 109.

Samuel Butler
(1835–1902)

1 . XD RZOJ ZK RZIJ XD RDOJ:

QRR VJQKDS ZK QCQZSKX ZX,

QSY QRR MJQRXMB ZSKXZSTX LDV

ZX.

2 . GJT QAAM DGJ CKMM CVK

CXZCV, HZC OC XKBZOXKU G WGJ

AQ UAWK UKJUK CA SJAY VAY CA

MOK YKMM

3 . KJMAV, BJWA XASVQV, SDA

YZEG ZY EZEA XFQ QUZVA QUSQ

YAAG QUAH.

4 . XZA ND SVQ GACW ZANXZC

SVZS CZEPVD ZAH VZD Z DSZSQ

CQPNDCZSEBQ.

5 . BJC TNLUQC NV BULC

GIPBJMID ICOCU ENCQ ULI

QZNNBJ.

6. TQOR QE TQIR HTJWQUZ J
YQATQU QU HFCTQK JUB
TRJGUQUZ PNR QUEPGFSRUP JE
AUR ZARE AU.

7. RZGI ZW VCI QHV FG MHQLZPK
WTGGZDZIPV DFPDRTWZFPW GHFO
ZPWTGGZDZIPV YHIOZWIW.

8. IO NTUEZ JFBXN YX WYGN I
XECIZ QFR FC I SFQZ ACFT KJYDJ
WYAN JIX QNUICENQ.

9. UVM RMQU GBED BQ VM JVL
TECMQ UVM QTEGGMQU ETLXSU
LP GNBSW WL UVM GLSWMQU
JEN.

10. RGO SNHEQI CY BYR PBYZ
OBYNMG RY HO OVSOFRX KOR
PBYZ OBYNMG RY COIQCO
HORZOOB RGOD.

11. VJI ETI NIBFELN ZETGFZVFET VJMV M PMT NJELWH JMGI FN VJMV TEVJFTY FN VE XI VMOIT VEE NIBFELNWA.

12. AVPRLKR VA LCQ UPSUFA QUKQ, ULY VQ VA QUKQ QGUQ VA OCPYRL, LCQ AVPRLKR.

13. WSS YTO WKAHWSP OGROXY HWK ZKCD YTWY YTO XBAKRAXWS QIPAKOPP CV SAVO AP YC OKNCF AY.

14. GDB FCP SD MJUG QYKKQJ TYKI OCYKI, ABK GDB FCP SD PDKIYPN TYKIDBK YK.

15. LSYEU FYQ WTQ NMSWTQU WTFW WTSZCTWU LQFY-SPMO WTQ NMSWTQU.

Answers on pages 109–110.

27

Joseph Conrad
(1857–1924)

1. ZFO TCQJ US TIQ CL BIYIAWO
US IQKZFCQE AOBIVLO
ODOXKZFCQE CL CQ CZ, IWW ZFO
YILZ IL HOWW IL IWW ZFO
SVZVXOL.

2. FRW XR XIW NOA FIRTW IWOSX
IOT ARX EWOSAWB FICEW ZRLAV
XR IRUW, XR ERYW, OAB XR ULX
CXT XSLTX CA ECDW!

3. MG URKME UI HTAKG DQA M
TEMVUGZ CUIUHG HT NKMEUAJ.

4. EXVVLK LV FIBW CX XCP QYBLDV
WX YLJP, SNW PGPAOSXRO PCMXOV.

5. PSZ HBBK MPS MPAAZ BS, XGY
BSKZ YIN VLDN UPS OSBVD IBV
YB DIBAYNS YIN DPLK.

6. KBN UVHII FNLOA BQ H CHJ EK
VSU QBAU HU XAII HU EK VSU
QYSAJLU.

7. PLBYO J HRUJY BC J VLFFBPXW
ABTTBINXV VFJAL, CBYIL BV
IRYCBCVC MFBYIBMJXXW RT
ALJXBYO HBVD ULY.

8. PCF SVBFG VI JVRQN CLJ
LZBLHJ XFFQ OGFLPFG PCLQ PCF
SVBFG VI JFQJF.

9. HGM D XWWH LG KDEG
BGNPZQGDLHG DQQWNEZTJ MW
IZB XWHHU.

10. NV ECQF EYG XCNE RCJF
UIFCZ WVZ EYR YG NEF
CGXYZCNYVP VW FQFZD EMRCP
LFYPT YP VMZ LFUIVMJFJ CPJ
NFRXFGNMVMG FAYGNFPUF.

11. BQG WGZRGY RO H
MDSGUOHBDUHZ MIDUXG IY GFRZ
RM OIB OGXGMMHUJ; KGO HZIOG
HUG LDRBG XHSHWZG IY GFGUJ
PRXNGAOGMM.

12. MO BUYTGMOP ZAC XLYMZ HX
KCKHLI HOC LYOV ZAC LMVG HX
VBHMUMOP MZV JUHHK.

13. DKVNRDI HCBZ RVZOHA KYOD
VK VNO MNCEIO KA
OLCIIOECVRKD GKEO VNCD VNO
HCDIWCIO KA DCSOP VEWVN.

14. HF JLYF, GP HF CZFGU-
GJRKF.

15. KUG PGEJ XNAZNWNDEZDG VW
DPNSG NX NZ NKX QGNZA E
QPGEDU VW WENKU MNKU KUG
DVSSFZNKC VW SEZHNZI.

Answers on pages 110–111.

Daniel Defoe
(1661–1731)

1. VEMPDK ZET CKGM MZLT
MLVAMPDK LV MZK FCNNI, MZEM
ECC WKV HNPCI FK MODEVMT LG
MZKO ANPCI.

2. GHTD PG LTWKHD NV RHW
RJPBVTWL RNSHV SPDH
RHDDNGZNWK RJTW LTWKHD
NRVHMG.

3. KOO HMZ BCCI HMLRBP CS HMZ
DCAOI KAZ RC SVAHMZA BCCI HC
VP HMKR KP HMZW KAZ CS VPZ.

4. BCFCGBHGW FAG FETFSB BNUX
QJ QWG PNBGFBG, FWP F MQQP
VGWBNQW MNLGB COGH VAGBGWC
GFBG.

5. WED VSXH WEGSM KDOWJGS
GS XGID GC QDJWE JSQ WJNDC.

6. RKH ZHNR VD IHG MSGGVR NWNXHGA RKHLY DSRH; RKH JVVA ALH HSYTE, SGA RKH ZSA ALH TSRH.

7. NCDK-TCNEJHFEUAR UN EMC CKKCFE AK FAGZJTUFC UR EMC MUBMCNE CPEJCVC.

8. AHLSMVI ML DFGDUL EMKFIQS SK SJI YDTSU KCCIQNMQX, CKT IEITU RDQ ML MQQKVIQS MQ JML KGQ IUIL.

9. OZQGQAQG UEK QGQNLV D ZETVQ ER JGDXQG, LZQ KQAPC DCODXV HTPCKV D NZDJQC LZQGQ.

10. TII FKZ XQWVFYNMYNW WBZQYA PZFS NCM ETYN FP NCTYGPKIYMWW PFZ ECTN EM CTUM.

11. FU NFEN FEK NOINF GB FSK

KSMU SK E JGGV EK QUVV EK E

WGQEOM SJ FU SK EJOESM NG

GQB SN HUWEIKU GJ GNFUO

ZUB'K GLSBSGBK.

12. O GPXC-APCL FCPTWOBG RJ

GWC ACJG ICBGNCFOB RB GWC

BOGRZB.

13. FEYQ PQT VLLECP EG EY GWQ

QTIXEYW FVM TQKQC GH ICNPSXQ

GEXX GWQM DHPQ GH UVM.

14. IVN VNAOVI UP VTXRZ

GABQUX AB IU WLAZO UTL

INXDNLB QUGZ IU UTL

MALMTXBIRZMNB.

15. MY VWQBRJA VQ RA

VWQBRJAZ MO VQ ITXA CQBW

VWQBRJA ZQBRJAZ.

Answers on page 111.

Charles Dickens
(1812–1870)

1. WB VPFUF XFUF QA OKI
YFAYJF, VPFUF XAGJI OF QA TAAI
JKXDFUZ.

2. DNMCYAB TPXYFI MA NKJP,
MFE ULIAYDP TPXYFI FPHA EKKC.

3. FRR VQ ZE AFWI MVXHIYE
ATHHIX TX VZY SYIFECE, VXRB
XIIHTXN KTYKZJECFXKIE CV
IWVLI CAIJ.

4. WDADO SKPXD UPMO KCLX BP
BRPXD BP VRPT UPM RHAD
PLDWDF UPMO RDHOB.

5. OWLE BZHPM DVU OWNT ZF
LVDTHM, KAJ WJ WMF'J MZ TVMU
BZO JETD JZ MTT ZAJ ZB V
FTTNHT'M TUT.

6. UVLJL PJL UDT OUIZLO TG
NTJUJPFU NPFSUFSX: UVL
OLJFTEO PSM UVL OWFJA.

7. Z WZK OZK KFAFB VF Z PBSF
XFKPJFWZK LK WZKKFB SKPLJ NF
LI Z PBSF XFKPJFWZK ZP NFZBP.

8. ZGUKO BUC XGGCD BTK
LKTWBEUQO WIK SKDW GA
TKAKTKULKD.

9. GYZVJRUZNE AYWW ZNSFU
VJRUZNE JXN JH OJXRNURSROU
SRE GSE JH NVU AUUT YH NVUFU
YZ SRENVYRB NJ MU BJN ME YN.

10. HZO RYFHQOA VG LVHZOFA
AZCKK VUUCAYVICKKM DO
RYAYHOS QTVI HZO UZYKSFOI, CA
POKK CA HZO AYIA VG HZO
GCHZOFA.

11. HFRZR JW Y CJWTUE UP HFR
FRYT YIT Y CJWTUE UP HFR
FRYZH.

12. KFKHU GRCDP NHKDIRHK OW
NZPWIOIRIKJ IZ SK IGDI
THZBZRPJ WKNHKI DPJ CUWIKHU
IZ KFKHU ZIGKH.

13. CNCAL OFOL OUAI GIEU EMC
PUARW GX F KGICA UIC EMFI EMC
RFXE.

14. G ENAAEO EOGJVNVZ NM G
CGVZOJULM AKNVZ, XLA G
ENAAEO HGAJUVGZO BUJO MU.

15. WCSI PMWLAPJ MP AWZ
OMMSZ; WCSI IRIXFWLAPJ MP
IRAUIPBI.

Answers on pages 111–112.

Benjamin Disraeli
(1804–1881)

1. JQGL JU Q ZQE QNUWJ
AVZMXGC QEI AX HVGG GVMJXE
CUT AUWTM.

2. N SNU CRD VG UDA N HVKLWNH
NA GVIALLU RNG UD RLNWA; N
SNU CRD VG UDA N EDUGLWBNAVBL
NA GVIAQ RNG UD RLNZ.

3. DC DE LFHK WIEDWY CV GW
HYDCDHIX CKIP CV GW HVYYWHC.

4. YSJR RU BYUPOYK PNSY RU
LSODS EY UTTUGRHYORQ, RNS
CULR OCTUGREYR RNOYK OY FOIS
OL RU BYUP PNSY RU IUGKU EY
EMWEYREKS.

5. BOK TAZBO AL C ICBUAI CGK
BOK BGZDBKKD AL EADBKGUBT.

6. UNKZHR MUQ EADLNRQ MA
WZKQ BZMUZH AHQ'V IQNHV ZV
LQVJQEMNYZWZMT.

7. TN T ABXBDTR DYRB, XWQWEV
UTN IWXBV SUW WYAUK KW UTZB
OK.

8. PBKRZH SBT NLXHP RT KUF
HBZT YRK FPJM FPH CFRKS, KSBK
UH CBM SHBZ AZFC FKSHZT
KULGH BT CRGS BT UH TWHBO.

9. AMAWI HWRQCSUJRT RX
FATJCE GCEU DA UKA
HWRQCSUJRT RX ATUKCEJZEG.

10. CH NQLJ XR JP JIGLLJFDL
WLGBXP NB J WLGBXP ZUX
JIGLLB ZNOU CL.

11. IEWK ER QYKMEXFR, GFI IYFIL
ER WXYK QYKMEXFR ILJC IEWK.

12. KLKUX RSC ASJ S UYWAO OE
ZK GECGKYOKH ICOYB AK YJ
JIGGKJJTIB.

13. IXG WDGVI ZGBDGI HN
ZSBBGZZ OL AONG OZ NHD V CVL
IH JG DGVPK YXGL XOZ
HUUHDISLOIK BHCGZ.

14. CUKHYZBYX IYZUB ZUX
CUKHYZBYX MYCBAHY ZHY DEY
DNF KCWCMCPYHB FS IZU.

15. LZD JKPTI XQ QTHFL AXMD TF
XEH TPVXHKVID LZKL TL IKV
DMDH DVS.

Answers on page 112.

George Eliot (Mary Ann Cross)
(1819–1880)

1. W X Z U W O H   W T P   H E L F
W Y T P P W D O P   A T Z P X C H ;   K F P V   W H M
X B   G E P H K Z B X H ,   K F P V   Q W H H   X B
L T Z K Z L Z H U H .

2. X Z M X F   F Q W   Z A M O F   Y J Q N A Z W
D Y   T H   U D X H   D X   X F Z A M O F .

3. N I P   T N Z X K Q P T N   A Z C K V C A O P   X B
Q Z X Y N I   O C P T   C K   I H S D K   V I X C V P .

4. P   B Z J J L S L O F L   U J   W P H W L   Z O
D U Q L H   Z H   P   E S L P W   H W S P Z O   U O
W T L   P J J L F W Z U O H .

5. T F L J   C A U Z C P U Z W W   P W   D A I Z
C A U Z C B   J F L U   V P W J I M W J ?

6. E Y M X V   E Y B   Q X E D P O N K   L E Y   Y P
F P V X   U X E V   W P   D P N X   N C M S W   P Z
W S X C V   P U Q X L W N   W S E Y   D P J X .

7. PH PJJ YPA FOPA P QNNE RSWIZ FZMNOZ SZ JSPCZJ XSZ JXPOJ ENRH.

8. CPSVS UZ ATCPUAM CPHC NUBB IUBB H JHA ZT ZTTA HZ PHWUAM ATETYO CT QUAY QHGBC NUCP EGC PUJZSBQ.

9. TX TQ ZCQR GTHETHV KZCQMHQ JIR MXIZK GMSUQ QIMOSE DZ FCXTZHX.

10. QS UZLZHX UXL, SLX SCHWQ QS WZMX Z TWZJE UKLA ZLA Z MXVMXQ TWXZQW.

11. HZU NDAUKJ GRNZVJR CIR GRAUK OITH IR DTSRJ AJ ORZQ ZUX URRXJ IAH.

12. SXB MBKVMC ZA ZGB CJSN HL SXB RZKBM SZ AJQAHQQ VGZSXBM.

13. TKKH DCQK, PKXKC LK
UWZUSKG MA GMFPI CFIZD;
GKBFGK MP YZUD EMQ DZFPT FW
CFIZD UPG WDFBT DM FD.

14. DL CQVCHY WTPCDKY LWRT
LECL DN VT ECG JTTK SWTCLTW,
MDWMRPYLCKMTY VFRQG ECBT
JTTK QTYY YLWFKS CSCDKYL RY.

15. KBM BPIIUMYK JNLME, AUHM
KBM BPIIUMYK EPKUNEY, BPGM
EN BUYKNSZ.

Answers on pages 112–113.

Ralph Waldo Emerson
(1803–1882)

1. LROKOLXCK PZACH HUNCSGQK
XQ MQIXR OSG ODC XQ
DKZSBNCG HBZS OSG PKOM
ROZKH.

2. WDB QZOU POGXWOXB SIW
QYPP, SIW AOG GBKBV DOS
OGSUZYGX JWU QZOU SIW OVB.

3. V AKID PKJDWN JT TYODQYNF
SBY GVW OVED IT NY SBVA SD
GVW.

4. RM VFA DFAYS ZAYL XBL DFZYS
GARLXYV, VFA PATX JLLI RX
OPATLS.

5. CEODWCA YTOECWTDJT NJC TE
NKUD YT UENNEC TJCTJ YCQ
XMYWC QJYMWCA.

6. UYR QFRSU LSDIFNUE IV LRM
SFR PZMXJRC IV PRQNMMNMQC.

7. Q AQE AGKW HXEKRPLS FMQW
Q SRHM SLQVA ML QDPRHQWLK
FMLE ML DLHXALK Q
HXEBXSARKW.

8. ACITIDIJ OBR VJI GSTXIJIPO
UPIVGIY, OBR VJI TBRJSGCIY.

9. ZX DPX DNZDCO AXSSQHA
PXDJC SV NQFX, EYS HXFXP
NQFQHA.

10. XDZN ELW EGPOKZM ELW QDO
RETM GREKLMW YRM XRMMC DJ
GRELGM.

11. OEOHP RJV BY JV
BRGTYYBUBIBFP KVFBI SO BY
UTHV.

12. FGXP DUGTWUDF YBZYSF
EOHV TF SGTHW YHV MPPR TF FG.

13. JRL DGR DBB CLSRLXUGF
FDCBCLP MUGXN UL D SUTDPR UM
WCFHUSRGT.

14. Y KJLMVS LF Y OMJFGV ZLXC
ZCGT L TYI QM FLVDMJM.

15. BMSU RNU BZDR ZJ
WZQVDUXJ, JZV RNMR GD MXX
RNUVU GD RZ WZQ.

Answers on page 113.

Henry Fielding
(1707–1754)

1. QKYKG WGEUW WDK ALQ IDF
DLU GKLUFQ WF UEUNKVW WDLW
MFE PQFI DK DLU TQHEGKR MFE.

2. ZFRK EGX UYEGXEZ EOK IQK
PKUI UHKKIKGKOU FW IKE.

3. NKVUZINY SRAT URAN
LRAHOEIF RC GBN UOCJ GBVC
ZANHNZGY.

4. UXYZDN NJH PSJM J NJF GFZD
NJFH STTDTY, EXZ GZ
RXYZGVGSY FDFS.

5. HPVU F'O UXI IPEUZVW EI EDD
F'O IPEUZVW VUXMAP.

6. BJIFM UN EQF LTRUE JL FZUX
CN JLEFI CN EQF TJJE JL UE.

7. DF XRFW LFDRPLK PY KPMBL,
FH RPW AQL LFDRPLK CB
SBENPSBI.

8. AOKHNOQ UQOCH ILGOQHE ALQ
UQOCH QKPNOR MKFF NOCQ
QOCRLA.

9. FGZY FRJYC CRIH NRW GJW KE
OKXX UXGNIY CRI XKZY EMY
WYSKX.

10. EGW LHQPWFBW TK EGW
DWME GWCPM YM TKEWF
PWKWCEWP DS EGW
EWFPWHFWMM TK EGW DWME TK
GWCHEM.

11. OA EOFE PFT OAGUJPFSSD
ATCXGA FCIAGYJED KJSS MAFG
HGUYHAGJED KJEO ABXFS
WGAFETAYY UQ YUXS.

12. CWTO T QZJJD KGJJHC PMQO WG XG CWH CHMJN NH OWG NGBZJ'Q CHFU KHF VHOWZVA.

13. VA VD S TQQI GSWVG AQ AOLDA S RJODQZ JZAVOJYK QO ZQA SA SYY.

14. MYID QYUKTEID XEI TFUDP DFLYUDP, LYIJ XEI TFUDP VURQYUIG.

15. IAJFH UVZZ OEH IATF VJ AJF IAIFJS SKEJ SKF IAOS FZARCFJS ZAXFTO MEJ VJ HFETO.

Answers on page 114.

Robert Frost
(1875–1963)

1. E BEK ZTGG WJBXPTBXW

HXRJPX EGG QTW GTIX PJ PQX

HXRXGJUBXKP JI JKX UEYP JI

QTW CJHL-PQX ZTWQCJKX.

2. HTWDS'O DSH WLMSD XUTRH

EBW UBZH: L PBY'D JYBN NSHWH

LD'O ULJHUF DB MB VHDDHW.

3. OD QEKFF GYKHC O XZD CRI

RL FMFKBQEODA O'MF SFZKDFH

ZWYRQ SOPF: OQ AYFC YD.

4. GFQM VA C EPCDM YGMXM,

YGMK SFZ GCNM HF UF HGMXM,

HGMS GCNM HF HCRM SFZ VK.

5. CUQIAOCZE CIQ NABQ C IAOJ

LCKJQI RJF RAEJQE JQ BZQR JFR

KF HAMQ JAE EFZ KJQ JCIYEJASE

KJCK UCYQ JAU IAOJ.

6. RDIB DS BYG FYOXLG ZG BYUXM ZG IGG UX AUSG UI TWG BD BJWBYI EGUXL UX OXT DWB DS SOHDJ.

7. GLIQ NTLG BV UBWQD, LDC RLIQ BG KWQA SKJA NLS.

8. RCJKZFYLT YN MZTHYTH ZVLJTC JTFYB OLJ'XR KZJHMF LT.

9. JVUKU HKU JVKUU ZKUHJ JVFSZI FS JVU PGKWX: JVUKU FI KUWFZFGS, JVUKU FI IEFUSEU, HSX JVUKU FI ZGIIFC.

10. MJK GYEDT DF E CWTOKYHRB WYXET; DM FMEYMF CWYPDTX MJK NWNKTM ZWR XKM RL DT MJK NWYTDTX ETO OWKF TWM FMWL RTMDB ZWR XKM DTMW MJK WHHDAK.

11. Y HEMI BRFUNUQU RJ QLKGSK
XKMURFU BARUKF QR CKBNCK
LAR AYU QAK PKQQKM GYLIKM.

12. HGZFNFOA RVOGQ LJ MSOP
JOIJNO YGQO SFPYA KIL CIP'Y
FPYOPC GPC ZFAA SFPYA KIL CI
FPYOPC.

13. WB TUJVQHR MLQYPMAZZB
OQRPY PUAJE L ILB, BUA DLB
OXOHYALZZB ROY YU WO L WUEE
LHI TUJV YTOZXO PUAJE L ILB.

14. O BPSIXROK PJ O ROD FYX
OIFOLJ EHRHRUHEJ O FXROD'J
UPEKYBOL UZK DHWHE
EHRHRUHEJ YHE OAH.

15. X MCLIDXM CZ X FXU KYY
LDYXJFCUJIJ KY KXSI WCZ YVU
ZCJI CU X BPXDDIM.

Answers on pages 114–115.

Kahlil Gibran
(1883–1931)

1. SEN SLMDC HLNRS FRP BZ EN
QET QTMDU FRZSNL PT TPN, RPU
QET QTMDU GN FRZSNLNU GC
PTPN.

2. MGV HSBW KVX NSXXNW DYWC
MGV HSBW GA MGVF
UGJJWJJSGCJ. SX SJ DYWC MGV
HSBW GA MGVFJWNA XYEX MGV
XFVNM HSBW.

3. JDJUV AIS QW EXP AJS; PSJ
QW IXIOJ QS EKJ FIUOSJWW, EKJ
PEKJU IWNJJZ QS EKJ NQHKE.

4. CTFCJ AK B XPPN HAUXUPKK
CJBC CPBYJPK FK CW GP
YWUCPUC AU WFT POPTSXBS
EAVP BUX KJBTP DACJ NPWNEP
CJP KBZP JBNNAUPKK.

5. LD CFU OZREO FH UILZDU
QIRC JFWZ QRVV LD HWVV UIR
UILZDU UIEU LD WCSWRCPIEGVR?

6. AZ AY KVHH ZL JAXV KMVI
PYRVC, GWZ AZ AY GVZZVE ZL
JAXV WIPYRVC, ZMELWJM
WICVEYZPICAIJ.

7. VKGKDAHTMS TH VTZTGV QADK
MEFG SAN PFG; RDTYK TH
MFLTGV OKHH MEFG SAN GKKY.

8. IQZ YUJ CLJ AQMR HUQG
MIDBL IQZU BLDNVUJT YR
NDKDTX YUUQMR YUJ RJTC
HQUCL.

9. NEY RGKQGMGHZQHY AM LZQ
GR QAN JEZN EY ZNNZGQR, DCN
OZNEYO GQ JEZN EY SAQKR NA
ZNNZGQ.

10. VNX EGZZNB JGV UIHNUKI
XCNZ BOI PZZNEIZB ZNU JPLB PB
LUNH BOI OIGUB NL BOI DXPJBV.

11. YT CMZL VP BVMD SNQIYTK,
SLYTIYTK YG LNQP CMDXODOX.

12. QTLUFT UL DJYB VB YUBT;
UPQUBBTFTPMT UL DJYB VB
QTJID.

13. YKFB YF VJXB VP PBF ZBPVKFX
OPX WPJBAFD, YF XFMJWF VKF
BJSEFX PO PJX FBFSGFA.

14. LW VBLHHVSLQJNW JT L QSMQI
QILQ ILT GNTQ JQT QVODVS.

15. FBFQ JYH NW DFFE WJYW
PGBF UEGLH EGW NWH GLE
RFAWJ SEWNP WJF JGSQ GC
HFAYQYWNGE.

Answers on page 115.

54

Oliver Goldsmith
(1728–1774)

1. UGZ KRQ FHWRKA R CWDDWH
XWHJGQ TEDA UGZH PESW DARQ
TEDA UGZH PEFX.

2. WRINSOB ROS RWIRNB GZOS
OSRXN LZ HSL R GRD PDLZ
LOZYCWSB LURD ZYL ZT LUSG.

3. FZ VNB CLOL MN XUYL KFMMKL
ZFPELP MUKY, MELV CNBKH MUKY
KFYL CEUKLP.

4. BDM RGBR CMXXMLX RGM
MLFAEKMLR AV CNVM NLPZMBXMX
AWZ UMXNZM AV CNHNLD.

5. Z AYWF FWFNHBIZPQ BIKB'R
YAJ-YAJ DNZFPJR, YAJ BZOFR,
YAJ OKPPFNR, YAJ MYYCR, YAJ
XZPF.

6. LYM CRXLWM TYRSY
XMVWRXMU LQ DM MCMX
JWPXAMA RU USPXSMEN TQXLY
LYM UMBLRBME.

7. FYPNW HWT PVQOK QSYVRT
WNANE CN THXNT.

8. UJ QEVJ RFJEQJF YEXWI QD
YJFIAEBJ DQLJFI QLEQ UJ EFJ
LEYYC QLEW XW JWBJEPDFXWR
QD SJ ID DAFIJTPJI.

9. IJWELN NQSCW HOB Q WALI
ECKCPWC QZQJPWB BFLOHAC,
BULOZU QB AQWB Q WOFC LPC.

10. WIX WCYX YVX HO VAXXFI RV
UHW VH DYFI WH XTACXVV HYC
SQUWV QV WH FHUFXQB WIXD.

11. HLNBN HNKEVL KSG RBNNGWP
BNCZS, FWSVNSVPNSV RKCEX.

12. XBQKILWAQD QW P
LQWQICKBKWCKL SVHHKBSK
GKCJKKI KOTPNW; NVFK, PI
PGEKSC QICKBSVTBWK GKCJKKI
CRBPICW PIL WNPFKW.

13. ONQC T MD HQKQUDTCQH, T
MSOMRW STWKQC KF UQMWFC
VQAMXWQ TK AMC KNQC HF CF
NMUD.

14. WGPWOG HGOJPQ LQWMPXG
UBGA RBGE BSXG AP PRBGM
QPJGO CFR RBGQHGOXGH RP
TPWE SZRGM.

15. NVD VJXKQ ED FTQQ EZNV
VTFFB FKJQFDANQ ZY LZDE TKD
GJKD FWDTQZYS NVTY NVJQD
AKJECDC EZNV HKXZNZJY.

Answers on pages 115–116.

Nathaniel Hawthorne
(1804–1864)

1. JPWI ABPIH QKID CH RCJ
BINKIH PJH HTNUQG RITPXU.

2. B PBF'M MNDQ PBW SI SDTUIG
BFG VITUMR DFGIT B GDFERIBV
NT UF B XDTTNZ NX YRI XUIQG,
ADMY BM ZIQQ BM DFGIT B VUQI
NX PNFIW.

3. VQWWBUHRR BU IVBR DTAXK,
DVHU BI OTLHR, OTLHR
BUOBKHUIQXXM.

4. BAST ZC JSB WTZAB TY E
UBYHBAJZTD ZD JSB IZUUTU.

5. PUPFR NMTNUNTLZD WZB Z
SDZEP XI VNDD NM XWP YIFDT
ZMT NB NOSIFXZMX, NM BIOP
FPBSPEX, YWPXWPF WP EWIIBPB
XI HP BI IF MIX.

6 . OH D GDE XBZB RQZB CH
WOPOEK HCZBPBZ LBZB, LB XCQWJ
ECY MDZB DICQY LOR CHHRNZOEK.

7 . Z AQDZX'Y FJZYURUK
FQXYRYUY, ORCL ZX QXRQX, QM
Z YLBRLY QM FQZUY.

8 . TLMI TA PMRR FAMR AEIMIA, ILA
EKRUH BFKSJH IK DSURH M LKSEA
KJ, UE ILA DFKMH WKSJHMIUKJ
KJ TLUPL JAMFRN MRR ILA BSURI
KW ILUE TKFRH FAEIE.

9 . UOBVEUYSOUU EU LSO LV NYO
AZCBENEOU CDN NL ESUDEIO BLMO.

10 . MKY IXTS VYXVNGTY YXBV IA
TNMYZWMHZY WZY ANZVM, MKY
RTYWVHZWGTY MINT IA PZNMNXQ;
VYDIXB, MKY QZWMNANDWMNIX IA
IXY'V AWENTS WXB AZNYXBV;
WXB TWVMTS, MKY VITNB DWVK.

11. SQBXTBK QJG GQJRMGB DPAU
ZTRM UETJTRU TB RMGS.

12. LBDJ SA JBF EYSVF YM AYRO,
LBFR JBF LYCUH UDVTA JBF FDC
YM JDAJF?

13. CDGQG RK OM KSWD CDROH
RO JFO'K OFCSQG FK F KGCCZGN
FON ESZZ QGKMZUG GRCDGQ EMQ
HMMN MQ GURZ, GVWGIC FC CDG
UGQP JMJGOC ME GVGWSCRMO.

14. YSCXI VP QWU GLIPU XJ QWU
OXIYT, SKT KXCXTB GSK ZUTTYU
OVQW VQ OVQWXLQ CUGXZVKR
FIXFXIQVXKSQUYB CILQVJVUT.

15. GUW ZWKG PC YK ZWSVO
YVCSG GP FSW, LUNG NV
SVWJTDWKKSZAW NZKYDFSGE GP
TYG GUW LPDKG GP FWNGU.

Answers on pages 116–117.

William Hazlitt
(1778–1830)

1 . GZX ZB XMI BFAX KY
RKHTIDBFXZKH, HKX XMI YKKS.

2 . ECUVN YCU XHF XULLHFG
ECNLVNBJNV, XULLHFG UECNOV.

3 . DBX UNZX TX CN, DBX UNZX TX
MJG CN; DBX KFLRXZ TX JZX, DBX
UNZX VXRLFZX TX BJSX.

4 . QRKY H XRNYO EKHLKL XC SK
H LTSPKEX CW ECYXBCAKBLU, NX
EKHLKL XC SK H LTSPKEX CW
NYXKBKLX.

5 . GVVS BJ UIME BAV UJJT RMNN
JP JBAVXG XIBAVX BAIE BJ
VWBJXB BAVMX ILLNIOGV.

6 . INR GFI TK DORGBECH
STCBEBIB EC URECH DORGBRZ.

7. SGTKFQZPT ZV BTRTG TEVU
FBWTVV ZC PEB SEVV ZCVTWI LII
ILG GTEVLB.

8. DCW UXD SL ERLW RN DS ZVSK
CSK DS WVYSP U ERDDEW UVA DS
WVAGXW OGJC.

9. TFTEKUAT NA H QEUCR SHO
BST ZUCTE BU BSEUC RNEB; ANAT
UPB UI BTA SHFT BST
NAQJNAHBNUA.

10. RZ DZUZO SB PDTXFMDK RZEE
CDXME RZ WZPJZ XB XFMDQ
PABCX XFZ HPDDZO BY SBMDK
MX.

11. KJS YURS UO YZGSTKH ZD
KJS YURS UO UKJSTD; KJS YURS
UO NUIST ZD KJS YURS UO
UWTDSYRSD.

12. VFM CSTV TZHMAV EMSEHM
DGM XMAMGDHHO VFSTM KFS
VFZAB CSTV FZXFHO SQ
VFMCTMHJMT.

13. RN MRI FLHNEAJTFNP
RDVPNTQ DP XFPYTB
FLHNEAJTFNH SB IYRNEP.

14. CD VHB ED CRJJRPT IQ IDJJ
H ZIQYB ICRXD, PDSDY IQ KDHY
RI VQYD IKHP QPXD.

15. ZJ HEJ GTF WHFAWKAJS FT YJ
EAIPF DGRJWW ZJ OHG UETCJ
TFPJEW FT YJ MDAFJ ZETGI.

Answers on page 117.

Aldous Henry Huxley
(1894–1963)

1. BJSVR ET RJMRX, LMR TREQQ
BJSVRSJ, ZJHN V KJVGREGVQ
KHEAR HZ IESC, ET TEQSAGS
VLHMR RJMRX.

2. WKQ NBMV YNXAMQWQMV
YNBPRPWQBW AQNAMQ OGQ WKQ
TQOT.

3. QIFHL EZ SZH FYILY HZ YVULH
CYFIJLY HMYP IOY UBSZOYE.

4. XOUIA GOU NAPQAWA XOCX
XOAK CLA AMJPYIQWAPK QR XOA
LQEOX CLA EARALCPPK XOUIA
GOU CJOQAWA IUBAXOQRE.

5. OKIOPLOSGO LX SHA NVEA
VEIIOSX AH RHQ; LA LX NVEA
RHQ MH NLAV NVEA VEIIOSX AH
RHQ.

6. AWLLXYDKK XK FXTD EPTD-
KPUDNAXYM RPV MDN WK W IR-
LZPJVEN XY NAD LZPEDKK PB
UWTXYM KPUDNAXYM DFKD.

7. VN XAE BNJ, IUIZQ FDL AE
LDTNOINL; XILGI VXI GNLEVDLV
TNTPODZAVQ NK BNJE.

8. NYZC JONGE FKAEUZ JGBK GE
GINYZC AESAEACK HGLGHACR
SYQ CGPACU CJAEUZ SYQ
UQGECKT.

9. OLPFOX QOZZWDRHH OXUOTH
XBBSH ZYRPPT HIFOXWE WD
LBJZOYWHBD UWPQ PQR
BCRYLBJZRDHOPWBD VBY
JWHRYT.

10. EPK MDWKJE VKYA JS
CDEJKMM YTYDJME EPKBMKWLKM.

11. ZADYD VYD MDP PAE PEICJ
SEZ YVZADY XD ZVQDS GS
VJICZDYB ZAVS GS
HYENGSTGVCGFL.

12. AYVFX NVCQ VIWHFVCT, JY
MFTJFK NQJ QMWWKFP CJ
VFSVCK TJH!

13. ILPVP EQ QYUPILEDZ
OAVEYAQFJ CYVEDZ XCYAI
QYUPCYRJ PFQP'Q LXGGEDPQQ.

14. GBFBMLI BONXGBG LMB
LIQLPG IBGG NRJFCJNCJT UWLJ
RJB.

15. RIT CKTVGOYTG LQ
UHMLYVMST VYT VG HYTVR, UM
RITUY JVA, VG RIT CKTVGOYTG
LQ DMLJKTZHT.

Answers on pages 117–118.

Samuel Johnson
(1709–1784)

1. ISJ MTIOLTQ YQUWSIN RY ISJ
SOATM AUMF TLJ MRI YLRA
ZQJTNOLJ IR ZQJTNOLJ, DOI
YLRA SRZJ IR SRZJ.

2. EH YJE IFIT GIM LIDJYI STIJM
LG OYOMJMOHE.

3. DMWWTMCH YMK DMVU LMTVK,
ZQS PHETZMPU YMK VJ LEHMKUWHK.

4. GUHWJKLJYY UY DEGBDY
JBYUJP VNBL ZUPVTJ, SXP UV
VBWJY VNJ YNXPVHTV VX
JZJPDVNULC.

5. BJXLX WVKB HAIHZK NX H
KBLVTTAX NXBIXXM H GHBJXL
HMQ H KUM; IJDAX UMX HDWK HB
FUIXL, BJX UBJXL HB
DMQXFXMQXMRX.

6. NWQGQNQLS QL K LGTJO MO
YPQNP SHR EWDY QSVDWGKRG
KRJ BDWSQJKMUH KG ZHWO
LSKUU HIVHRLH.

7. YPDBV'J CPGW KJ MVKHNYWI
MKLO LOW MKHI PHI JMPVLOS
MKLO LOW JRH.

8. PHOYQ ROI NJPY RGY NAY
AYRXJYWN ZSGIYOW HM KJMY,
ROI NAY SOAREEJYWN HM RKK
PHGNRKW RGY NAHWY BAH ARXY
PHGY HM YJNAYG NARO NAYQ
VOHB AHB NH SWY.

9. UEIC SU LCD ULQLD WH OSHD
LCQL RWRD QVD CQBBZ JEL JZ
LCD QRLSISBQLSWR WH ICQRAD.

10. CNYAGCX BOC SQ YHDTF
XHQOY IAGBA GU CNY HGXAY.

11. CI CM DVIIVQ IG MYAAVQ
HQGZJ IBXZ IG OG CI, XZO
BXFFCVQ IG DV MGPVICPVM
LBVXIVO IBXZ ZGI IG IQYMI.

12. AP UAV UIELG LV WV I ONPIL
WPIC VK OVVW IL VJRP UECC
JPFPN WV IJTLAEJO.

13. MXOR XV U AXMM JQXEQ
HPHR PO KV EUH SRUG DP
VJUMMPJ JXDQPKD NXMIXHN.

14. PSLZ BW UEZ OBWNSI SY UEZ
YSSP RAN UEZ YSPPM SY UEZ
OBWZ.

15. JZ LTANZRB JYB IZHVBO
TZTBOJF ZG ZAAZNJKOLJP COV
ECJEY JYB IZZV JYCJ LF SLJYLO
ZKN NBCEY LF JYB INBCJ CNJ ZG
HLRLOI.

Answers on pages 118–119.

Rudyard Kipling
(1865–1936)

1. IAA WJD TDYTAD ASFD BZ IUD
XD, IQG DRDUPYQD DAZD SZ
WJDP.

2. TGIIGS UIGKTCV PGI DGKIHVCP
EP UYFU'H DGKI XFUKIV, TKU
AGX'U CVXA EU UG DGKI
XVEBYTGIH.

3. UTK ZHGGHKZU EFXPB SPB
XPBPCK P SGKYKA XPB; OIU HU
BKKJZ P YKAQ SGKYKA EFXPB UF
XPBPCK P VFFG.

4. GVMWP ZMK UCK OVPU TVGKMLAI
WMAE APKW FJ OZRYNRW.

5. KDFWXQT DFX QZB YDWX PR
TVQKVQK "ZU UZG PXDNBVJNA"
DQW TVBBVQK VQ BUX TUDWX.

6. LPSDK TSBBPX LJ O VOD ENF XSXD'C EOZ NSB VIBCOUNP SB MSTP POCSDK OD PKK ESCNFIC BOMC.

7. ZD KUHMDRW KZD IHWKDWK CZB KUHMDRW HRBXD.

8. CRM QIX XGLGU JGBB DNGX CRM'LG ROGXGH I NGBB, NRD YRRX CRM QIX OMJ KIQE JNG BPH.

9. OMQR DMQRU DWGG ONFE WU F QFU'O QRQMIE WS NBRE MULR DFGJRC CMDU F ONIRRN.

10. C ZTQCK'N OFPNN YN QFWL QTJP CWWFJCUP ULCK C QCK'N WPJUCYKUA.

11. FE EFV IBMFXC EO HMFIVT HBVF IBV YTUCC MC YTVVF.

12. VRI FKRNM JSR JXPJS NF
JSRH PILRXFJNIL ZJ, NIL UDVRI
NF JSRH JSZIM VRI UDPBL BZMR
JD PILRXFJNIL ZJ.

13. XNMQYEZC NR A AU RG
RPEYZC'D YPMDZ, SME RADECZDD
AU RG PHU.

14. GQ BMZ OKAR RM OGA BMZY
DKRRNLC, RKTL KAW OMYT BMZY
DNMMJGA' FZAC.

15. L VHKLQ FM HQBZ L VHKLQ,
RIW L OHHG SFOLJ FM L MKHTX.

Answers on page 119.

Henry Wadsworth Longfellow
(1807–1882)

1. FXRDG AK GYR DXG IJ
SRFALLALF, SPG FXRDGRX GYR
DXG IJ RLUALF.

2. CZFO ATZAJT SZVJG FVHHTTG
WM FCXJJ OQWMLF, WY OQTU
STBT MZO OBZVIJTG SWOQ LBTXO
XCIWOWZMF.

3. AE AF KAMMATNQE EW JDWP
OE PBOE IWIXDE QWLX VXCADF;
AE AF QXFF KAMMATNQE EW JDWP
EBOE AE BOF VXCND.

4. OV NQOD KUHXF W PWV PJDN
YONQYH SY WVAOX UH QWPPYH.

5. BZGGZJ LUR BSNKUYK LGK
BIGZUO, LUR CLISKUI KURQGLUYK
SB OZRNSHK.

6. KFW WZWTNHUN VUTWM UJH
HRKLWM, YFLVF XWJ VUOO
HTRHDWTN, UTW KFW YWLDFKM
UJH VARJKWTSALMWM AC KFW
VOAVP AC KLXW.

7. OBL REON SH OBN DAWWAV
REON AR EXX; SVOA NEDB XSRN
HAWN TESV WMHO REXX.

8. YNE UCQ ISE RSZJE HUS MVEJ
UCJ ZKQSK SI ZJ UN HUS MVEJ
CE SOO, EUN RZEEYN GSIN.

9. SYZUU AMDUEBUA SYUZU XZU:
SYU RMZAS LR AVUUBY, SYU
AUBLEJ LR JUAMZU, SYU SYMZJ
LR SYLCQYS.

10. GLOB OYGV ALWWLH XEU
GLOB QLOOXEU, VTLYDT XWW XIB
OXUB LA QWXN.

11. BTT ZIYK CDKPEODX MC ME
YEMIE. BTT ZIYK JBEOPK MC ME
JMCVIKJ.

12. XQ ZQO XAILF; OEA UQIXAZ
KQKAZOG VIF.

13. IWXDD SJGXYUXBA, IWXDD
OMTIMXBA, DYSTB WZ DSKZT SBV
WZ QSXW.

14. RG KUZHZKJTH, RG QZGGTH,
RG LJPXT, RG ZXX JURGFL, JUT
LBAHTQT TYKTXXTGKT RL
LRQAXRKRJP.

15. BCH CHZLCBN QK LVHFB UHT
VHFYCHJ FTJ AHRB, SHVH TXB
FBBFZTHJ QK NDJJHT GMZLCB,
QDB BCHK SCZMH BCHZV
YXURFTZXTN NMHRB, SHVH
BXZMZTL DRSFVJ ZT BCH TZLCB.

Answers on pages 119–120.

W. Somerset Maugham
(1874–1965)

1. FKZAH EJ DEIA C JEBNP JAZJA
MENPKVN MPELP HKV LCZZKN
FCIA C LKFODANA VJA KG NPA
KNPAU GEWA.

2. DXWBHSXCP XW DVBXHCP XD
YXOH LW XSVW ZXSJHS XW L
GVTDH VK BLSJD.

3. IZ I EMQQWP CIPZT NQW
JKNBYE WIZ VMJWYT OBZ QNZ
ZNN VWYY, IQE ZIYG VWYY OBZ
QNZ ZNN VMJWYT.

4. EKW GNCVW ML IVCEVDW PF
PEF WLLWIE MJ IKNDNIEWD.

5. CYGD YV VW CLJTDCU
NWOAJWCCDQ IU NXLOND AXLA
YAV NWOQMNA NLO ID IMA L
EDJEDAMLC YSEJWPYVLAYWO.

6. VZ TXSQEYD VUD UTWEV ZO
YDTCEAL EG VZ XZAGVYQXV OZY
NZQYGDMO T YDOQLD OYZI TMIZGV
TMM VUD IEGDYEDG ZO MEOD.

7. OGUOZG QKZZ FUCGBKCGF
WUVIKYG XUT BLG IUUE XUT
LSYG EUHG BLGC, DTB FGZEUC
BLG LSVC BLGX LSYG EUHG XUT.

8. OUYYKUIJ KC U TJYX IEEM
GDKVI, ZBG K GDKVP KG'C U
OKCGUPJ GE OUPJ U DUZKG EL KG.

9. WNXGHFNXGCVHGL HW DXVL
WNXGHFNXG GUCG EKJW LDK KB
GUN PEDXY PCL.

10. CPAOA WU EXGQ EXA CPWXT
HMEFC LPWZP W HD ZAOCHWX,
HXK CPWU WU CPHC CPAOA WU
NAOQ GWCCGA HMEFC LPWZP EXA
ZHX MA ZAOCHWX.

11. WNRWYN CXZ KRD JRS OSTLTOTXP, GDL LFNK RBYK QCBL WSCTXN.

12. PMDDMR QSRQS JRC WMMC RJFTAS KYVV CM J VMF FM DJZS FES XYVWAYDJWS MG VYGS RMF FMM CYGGYPTVF.

13. FR FQ QJVHRJLO RU RLJFE UEWQWVD RU ZW EU TULW JDDWIRWP ZO IWEQHLW RAJE ZO MLJFQW.

14. KBA RMES PR N KXMEVSARMUA HMRRARRPMD, NDG TBAD UND GAJASMHAG PK BA SMRK KBA CNXGAD ML AGAD.

15. WNTBPQWJ KXNTJ TLDTQA AX VPJH PJ AMTPB MOEYWJHE W DTBVTQAPXJ AMWA TJCFPEM KXNTJ XJFG MXDT AX VPJH PJ AMTPB YOAFTBE.

Answers on pages 120–121.

Ogden Nash
(1902–1971)

1. YD TI LUNISTU VZCD BSVVZWT
IW AIINE HJNFDA BSEU.

2. WMDRMJEE KYRXL XUSJ PJJV
UII MYRXL DVOJ, PCL YL'E RDVJ
DV LDD IDVR.

3. I OITVZE VM I CUVW RQTXQMNL
UQW QUZE QO RJVZLSNU KCW QO
TIU, BQTIU, IU QRRIMVQUIZ
IUVTIZ, IUL WJN RQTTQU RQZL.

4. OY EWBT TOLW OJ SYTR
JBMWQ SYW JS UBMW B ZHBEEWT.

5. OKGF KZ THV BEQKTD XFFT
VHOR VBEV VBF YET BEZ LWZV
IENFR VBF GOHHC.

6. APQM PR RUMDDPHI YTKH Z
RUMD TG RPUUPHI PH Z NSZPG,
ZHY PU PRH'U USMGM.

7. LBWOW AT FKGC FKW DRC LF

RZBAWYW BRMMAKWTT FK LBAT

LWOOWTLOARG NRGG, RKH LBRL

AT LF BRYW R ZGWRO

ZFKTZAWKZW, FO KFKW RL RGG.

8. ML BFFT JLGI KQIIAQOF

RIAKKAXO CAMZ YLDF AX MZF

YLDAXO SGT, CZFXFDFI JLG'IF

CILXO QNKAM AM, CZFXFDFI

JLG'IF IAOZM, HZGM GT.

9. FBCCLBTX LK EIX BQQLBUSX GR

EVG OXGOQX, GUX GR VIGF UXNXC

CXFXFMXCK MLCEIZBWK BUZ EIX

GEIXC UXNXC RGCTXEK EIXF.

10. MH ASI RBVU US DZU UJZ

XSKU SIU SH QMHZ, RJA UJZ

UJMVD US OS MU MK US CZ B

DSKKMLZY CA OBA, BVO B

DSKKMLZZ CA VMDJU.

11. OXWOFX YAW YWSD CLKKLJZ

EWYJ ZXK OTLE VWSX KATJ

OXWOFX YAW YWSD CKTJELJZ GO.

12. ODMWEXC JWMW REQWEXWP XH

ZDNW ILRUPMWE LDOOK FK SRQRES

XLWZ CHZWXLRES XH RSEHMW.

13. MSI FLF ASH OPVF JLDH RT

TP URNS WRLNBQHTT PY

UPDHUHQA RQOHTT LA MET AP

EDPLF VHIGPQILXLOLAI.

14. RAF DFXDQF OAX RACEY RAFJ

GBE OCES KD BAFBS XU RAF

LBGFW BLF FMFLJZXSJ OAX ABW

FMFL OXE B ZFR.

15. BVOOGT SWT VI QMTZ NFY MSKT

BTX IF BSZN ETFEGT XMSX TKTDN

ZTQ ETDIFZ NFY BTTX DTBVZOI NFY

FC IFBTFZT TGIT SZO YIYSGGN VI.

Answers on page 121.

Dorothy Parker
(1893–1967)

1 . AUH XJE HMTHX UK UH;
AUEIFMJFQUKB UE EUNCWS
FJWUEHXIKUFE AUHX AYMVE.

2 . QVPZ CA GMA GMDYJN D SF
EDNAZ GV IYVE: DTHAYANN,
NVZZVE, S QZDAYT, SYT S QVA.

3 . CBPYP'L ZBP UOA ZBOZ EKSGH
POLP O BPOYZ GMRP O LOZMA
JKCA?

4 . PQU NUVP CMD PT OUUL
JQHGABUF QTEU HV PT EMOU PQU
QTEU MPETVLQUBU LGUMVMFP,
MFA GUP PQU MHB TZP TK PQU
PHBUV.

5 . MX'E FNX XTG XZCDGOMGE
XTCX LMII WE, MX'E XTG
KGEEGE.

6. GYUGDY XVU MU ZVRBJT
YFHYYM PK YBMWOLBHY; JUM,
AUO L PLB ZVLZ TUDRHRZT
RBTWOLBHY.

7. YK VQS VZLS KJT NUSBG
KJT'GS QZN, NQZMSGZEX BEO
NZXQZEX, BEO QS MJUN QZN
IBNNZJE ZN ZEHZEZVS, TEOKZEX-
PBOK, LBFS B EJVS JH VQZN: JES
JH KJT ZN PKZEX.

8. AKF AMY JYNA CFXLAUGLB
MYIEN UZ AKF FZRBUNK
BXZRLXRF XIF "VKFVW
FZVBYNFE."

9. RQRBZ ATQR'K JPR ATQR
SRHTBR MD G FIAARB FBRKK.

10. SGO JYU'W WLYJC YU GBX
XGEIY ULF WAZJNV.

11. DXRBUT, DXZWKTU, GWOPI, RXD, R FPOO, R AXZIF R XMCGU— P JUBUX ORPN DMUC AUUN GC MURXD, KWD ODPTT DMUC LROO DMU DPGU.

12. MHIMEH IXYOR RI UH IQH IA RZI ROGQYT: BIXQY IJ PHKP.

13. BUME SUUK NUBHV ETIE IQH TPKKHV EQHIMRQHM IQH UVOJ MIZH XHFIRMH VUXUKJ OUULM ZUQ ETHB.

14. PQOOQK OS PQ TQCO PR OIQVOR BQDKE OUDV TYQ YV D TSJQTQEE PQB.

15. DGRL OV SMV SMJUCK J'E OVVU OVSSVL XJSMGRS: PGZV, BRLJGKJSH, DLVBNPVK, TUE EGROS.

Answers on pages 121–122.

William Shakespeare
(1564–1616)

1. QP JQEJ BEAJR XVAPG, XPEAR,
EAN YVAJPAJ SR BSJQVDJ JQZPP
IVVN JQSAIR.

2. PB LMAP PRTS PB TZB, FHS
LMAP MAS PRTS PB KTG FB.

3. DLWAGGJL HDJURU SOJ YZRJL
FYUR XJKVYFJ XIJL RIJE SOJ
HYLJ.

4. BMP'Z MDRI BEPPMOZ IRDM RP
NOEZZ; AKMRO DROAXMZ JM
JORAM RP JEAMO.

5. YBMWHD MBCLD FH RGUUWM
DAW LWGRBV BP DAW SFHW.

6. HGQLZI DQHGTSH NAA PWYWXJ
IGTSAX CW DQHGTSH PWZNPX:
DGNH'I XTLW QI XTLW.

7. AT UMGJI ZACCV QGMMZ KCRHGKCZ X ZMTB VXUC XA LGKZA.

8. NXNHWEJN TYJ FYVMNH Y AHKNP CLM SN MSYM SYV KM.

9. DEOM FERYKN SF YEEP, XRN YSOMA RAFERYKN SF XMNNMQ.

10. MDL BUILXQL ZHMLX ZH OJSL UXXZQLXQL OLSBJWELB CDLX BOLWPUXK HWUIB.

11. KAB SBO LV LCU NEVB EX LV R FEJPNBM GRUJ, PLLM RJM ENN KLPBKABU.

12. YDFTF BLZFQ CLYDLA YDF ZFTO UBHXF IU BIZF H PLAE IU CLKP IT QARUU YDHY CLBB HNHYF LY.

13. OSIEVOU GKO DQQT ZSJC IS
IESDQ IEKI RVO.

14. VDU IUVVUA KMAV WB CMEWA
FL SFLYAUVFWG.

15. XK XN UHK NKSCUTL KYCK
FLNXSL NYHAZF NH VCUR RLCSN
HAKZXIL GLSBHSVCUPL.

Answers on page 122.

George Bernard Shaw
(1856–1950)

1. VUMMHUFD HT RQRJAUM

WDKUJTD HX KQVWHYDT XOD

VUIHVJV QS XDVRXUXHQY GHXO

XOD VUIHVJV QS QRRQMXJYHXB.

2. I KIL LMWMQ EMVVT AFS

ILAEJPLH SLEPV AFS NFLEQIOPNE

JPK.

3. RWYKY TKY RPE RKTOYNUYF

UQ SUMY. EQY UF QER RE OYR

HEZK WYTKR'F NYFUKY, RWY

ERWYK UF RE OYR UR.

4. SUPKP FB EL QLRP BFEAPKPK

SUTE SUP QLRP LC CLLO.

5. L RLW'Z ZFLB KZ WNF

MNRVCYFY HKFANSF L HNRLW'Z

XLBFYB.

6. Q GHCHPM IQHGYAN HX
VNRRNA RDQP Q BNQB
UQXRNASHNJN.

7. LM VLBS LZ PXLE BH JHNR,
IAPBLBQWR LZ PXLE BH BTR
HBTRA BTLEI.

8. BLQC-BMHIDCDHL LAMEQLB RB
VU BMHIDCDHL UVPLI ZLUZQL
SDVPURV EQRBPDAY.

9. G QJTQJEZGS BXSMLGP MU G
YXXL VXTWMFY LJHMFMEMXF XH
BJSS.

10. CRYE AMYBBN ZBYEEMAJ Y
UYP DJ ERYE NKV ERDPX RDU
CKAER ZBYEEMADPO.

11. LOFBA WCGS OB CQWT M
WOAAWS LCCWOBNQSBB MQK M
WCA CL PEFOCBOAT.

12. GSO ISO IRYGH FA FVC
VYDVCTF TWGGYFT, HWF VC
ISOOAF ZXCRR FVCEC RAOD.

13. WXH QHZQCH FXZ NHW ZO SO
WXST FZVCR BVH WXH QHZQCH
FXZ NHW GQ BOR CZZU JZV WXH
ISVIGLTWBOIHT WXHA FBOW.

14. COUAFB SK UCF QPZOAB'K
AFLFTYF JPA NFSTY
STUSVSBOUFB.

15. KR KV FPANJGTEV RT YJ
VKAXJGJ EAWJVV CTE PGJ PWVT
VRELKF.

Answers on page 123.

90

Robert Louis Stevenson
(1850–1894)

1. YU HN JMEN ZNCLJZND Q
DYZUTV DNTDN UB SNZDUTQE
JMNTYJYP.

2. ZES YCMZ GSUBZOPBR
UQHSXZBFSM UFS XCZ ZECMS DS
NC ZC MSSV.

3. XIIL EANG ZIJGK MA EANGKIUZ
FNM KWJGI EANG QANGJYI.

4. VRF PGTFOFXV ODFX ZGF
YHVFL VYOJ DL XDOFLPF.

5. CPX VZBKX GX VMJ IUZ QURXJ
BN VMBE BR ABFXZCJ.

6. XCZBWBDK BK XNLUIXK WUN
CQZF XLCVNKKBCQ VCL EUBDU
QC XLNXILIWBCQ BK WUCRAUW
QNDNKKILF.

7. PTWJ PKUGQL TC TEU TFQ
WBPLTBQD BP BQZTYZJL BQ
JZJUV MEGUUJY.

8. XYKHK LU WC REXI TK UC AEZY
EWRKHHBXK BU XYK REXI CN
VKLWS YBFFI.

9. LER YA E HXWEVIXW GQC
TYOWA RCV IDCR JXWEM ETCRW,
JIV DXYRHYDETTK JK
HEVHQGCXMA.

10. TAAFJ DBY EAAP YXAOEK MX
QKYMB ANX NDS, TOQ QKYS DBY
D CMEKQS TUAAPUYJJ
JOTJQMQOQY WAB UMWY.

11. AD ACIKME LDJMTREEB SV I
ZMAAMC ALSQN ALIQ AD ICCSKM.

12. UIUZWVQU MSIUT XW
TUMMSQN TVRUGFSQN.

13. L FAJLB TLAB HP CEPJ
UHRXEXBX ER UHRBJOTCLBERF
VGLB VJ ULRRHB UMAJ.

14. Q IVFAQHX RGFA GJ AQTVXA
HR HXWHREVXRQNTV JGF EVGETV
PKG PGMTW REVXW UVQFR
AGZVAKVF QXW XGA NGFV
AKVBRVTYVR AG WVQAK.

15. LJ QIQFR YGFK GJX MNFJQF
NE NPF ZLEQ, KN ZNBQ NJQBQZE
LB KN DQ KTQ OGLJQF; KN
ENFOQK NJQBQZE LB KN DQ
TGYYR.

Answers on pages 123–124.

Jonathan Swift
(1667–1745)

1. XNXBH QRI WXKJBXK OD SJNX
    SDIT, LVO ID QRI CDVSW LX DSW.

2. CXYYUYF UL T GTIJYG RKUSK
    YP BTY TDDJSGL GP WJLCULJ
    ZXG KJ GKTG UL RUGKPXG UG.

3. PMIBI QBI DIV VYKC LIQTPT
    OXBI PX LI CBIQCIC PMQF Q
    PQKSYFA OQF MQEYFA FXPMYFA
    PX TQZ.

4. IT RZI HCMM QZWF UTSIXFM,
    DSQ FBFNP RZI HCMM QZWF
    RTIFP; QVFNFLTNF, RTIFP CX
    DFQQFN QVZI UTSIXFM.

5. LR LF HFCPCFF KXO HF RX
    ERRCZJR RX OCEFXT E ZET XHR
    XK E RDLTN DC DEF TCICO GCCT
    OCEFXTCY LTRX.

6. DZYIQMOSH OU HBF QMLJFUH
HLOXWHF BFMRFS LFDFORFU MSE
HBF UOSDFLFUH IMLH ZV ZWL
EFRZHOZS.

7. U ZLTI GUA LT AIRIW EITT
UENAI VMUA ZMIA MI LT UENAI.

8. FUGM XMUXQM SBEM GUNM
PBNM SU RJAM SRMJN YJFAUG
SRBO SRMJN LUQQC.

9. JMYYFPDNN FN WJD
YDXYDWTMC YENNDNNFEP EU
LDFPV ZDCC ADHDFIDA.

10. DNY IAWVBAVI RXV EBXRLVNVY
NWQV DNY IHDAQWBSI, PF
PVSWBBWBS RH HUV GDDH.

11. ITGHZHV ECLHK QTH AHIHKQ
XHVKGOK MOHCKS PK QTH NHKQ
NVHF PO QTH BGEXCOS.

12. QTY AQLJICF AITYSY LU
APWWFHJGB LPD ZCGQA XH
FLWWJGB LUU LPD OYAJDYA JA
FJMY IPQQJGB LUU LPD UYYQ
ZTYG ZY ZCGQ ATLYA.

13. PUHO J XMDH IHOKDE
JZZHJME KO XUH PLMGS WLD CJW
AOLP UKC FW XUKE EKIO: XUH
SDORHE JMH JGG KO
RLOTHSHMJRW JIJKOEX UKC.

14. WQ WA DWQS DWQA FA DWQS
BFRPBA, DSWTS FBX VXOXB AP
FUQ QP TMQ QSPAX QSXE FBX
XZUNPEXY PV FA DSXV QSXE
SFOX NPAQ QSXWB XYHX.

15. DXGBG KW SRDXKSZ KS DXKW
PRBHV URSWDQSD, ATD
KSURSWDQSUN.

Answers on page 124.

Henry David Thoreau
(1817–1862)

1. K VKA GT ZGDO GA RZURUZXGUA

XU XOJ APVEJZ UI XOGAFT NOGDO

OJ DKA KIIUZQ XU YJX KYUAJ.

2. IK NVSSJD CJ IXDYJAD JAU

FXSF; DYKT VUK DYK YXWYIVT JZ

JAU PXUDAK.

3. KFWI NRGNBWKJTAJRTC

IERSIANI RK EIGU KJGFAD, TK YZIA

UFB VRAS T JGFBJ RA JZI WRCQ.

4. YV VQZSX VRJ VJ XCSQZ

VHWVU-JDS VJ XCSQZ QDO

QDJVUSH VJ USQH.

5. JYS THR HZTJWQ UJBFQ GN

QCS AGWSWQ THY CHW ZSHLYSU

HYRQCGYM JN HFWJZBQS KHZBS

FR ZGKGYM.

97

6. ISL FCS GPLV PS WPV BIKYV
CSY NLQV C MCY KLUDQCQPIS;
CSIQWLK PS WPV FCSSLKV CSY
LSEIRV C NIIY ISL.

7. TO OSHIWK LAEO PONKEAO QTI
TMK LNXO LI NXRAIBO TNK KIEP'K
OKLMLO.

8. DZS QNZZDU UDD VDDZ WDXASU
ECV SXXDXV NZB PCVBSPSNZDXV;
WDX UD BKSMM HGDZ UESP CV
UD NBB UD UES DWWSZVS.

9. ME MH EVG KCFFMCOG JP EVG
HJNT RMEV XCENFG EVCE KCZGH
EVG MXEGTTGDE PFNMEPNT CXQ
OMAGH WMFEV EJ MKCOMXCEMJX.

10. PBZN VEN PKLV KJ XKMF
FNSFNVL; VK FNSFNV TNNYOX QL
VK OQCN BJFNLE.

11. EW EG WTX NVJ AXWXLNEJXG
YTVW EG GVEA, JZW WTX YZLAG.

12. CW CZ ES CSWBUBZWCST
YPBZWCFS JFM HEU GBS MFPRQ
UBWECS WJBCU UBREWCLB UESI
CH WJBO MBUB QCLBZWBQ FH
WJBCU ARFWJBZ.

13. B CBE PBEEVH JK NBUA HV
NGPPKKA UE HFUN IUOK DFV
AVKN EVH NBHUNOR VEK OXUKEA.

14. P ADM FHBJUNB KTUNSA HA P
OGPSUF FHBJUNB XTUFGWA, P
AGP FHBJUNB APHTA.

15. ETTXK JAL HPL HALJKGALY
DLJMHP TN HPL DTAMY, HPL NBH
BOPLABHJOFL TN WLOLAJHBTOK
JOY OJHBTOK.

Answers on pages 124–125.

Mark Twain (Samuel L. Clemens)
(1835–1910)

1. LFHE HAN XNCOHBWFA HIX AFB
HL LCNNXA HL H KHLLHOIX, GCB
BDXM HIX KFIX NXHNJM WA BDX
JFAP ICA.

2. QIV NTJWAF SOI TSOKIO NX
CRN RC VJNT NTSW NTI
SWWXLSWEI XQ S AXXK IUSZCHI.

3. MLO MG FXO PMWF WFQAUALI
KAGGOQOLBOW VOFDOOL H BHF
HLK H SAO AW FXHF H BHF XHW
MLSN LALO SAJOW.

4. PBMYLPR VB PCCHV
ACTBAOLPR SV BMYCA DCBDZC'V
YSILMV.

5. FNDNLLBXM BL XKN GVXKNU VE
XYIBFP DKYFDNL.

6. IVS BMW ZVA HASK WAI GSMH
CAAH FAAOK VMK WA MHQMWIMCS
AQSG IVS BMW ZVA YMW'I GSMH
IVSB.

7. JMV YHQKGSQVRJ JMLJ MVGKF
TF HR HTX ILA SF RHJ JMV HRV
JMLJ SF FMTJ TK SR JMV QSRZ,
ETJ JMV HRV JMLJ SF FKHCVR
HTJ.

8. JMOR DRO MIN YXDBOR QMO
QORQM HDVVIREVORQ, QMO
DQMOXN IXO RDQ DG VCHM
IHHDCRQ.

9. KV WMWRQQT VRAHM PDCH
VJRE VJCHH NHHAM VD YCHYRCH
R ZDDI KPYCDPYVW MYHHFJ.

10. PLX BV QAM DXOJ LXBPLO
QALQ ROCVAMV, DH XMMSV QD.

11. UVPJ FUNBTX QB LTNX MT
TXU FTBBUBBQTX YJQPJ
TGMDVSGUB VSS MJU TMJUNB—
JQB SVBM LNUVMJ.

12. SAC OPDU LVBCQ LNUQC, VJY
CGAJ OPD BVJ YNQCPUC CGAE VQ
EDBG VQ OPD XTAVQA.

13. FBXDVPE OA MYYV, FBXDVPE
OA OIHEPAAOGP, CXF OF OA FBP
JOMBFDODM FBUF VYPA FBP
ZYER.

14. YAPRD, PXR JWQRJP MBV PY
HYDLRV ZTJTDAYQZBPTYD TJ PY
PRCC PXR JPQTHP PQWPX.

15. WDWQZ YER BEG E GWJQWX
EYCVXVFR: XF FKXGYEQX
BFQGWG, PVGB, ERN OFYWR.

Answers on pages 125–126.

Oscar Wilde
(1856–1900)

1. NG ND YKDLMC GA CNZNCO
VOAVBO NUGA QAAC YUC KYC.
VOAVBO YMO ONGWOM EWYMFNUQ
AM GOCNALD.

2. U JWAAJS TWCBSQWAH WT U
IUCLSQDET ANWCL, UCI U LQSUA
ISUJ DY WA WT URTDJEASJH YUAUJ.

3. ZGOA WF VKEO BTY YNSYHOF
RCBL BOKYCF.

4. IWUH IU EYNBU SOCPUYQUP,
IU GUUY HS SHU UYPU WNP N
CDKWF FS EYNBU OP.

5. ZBKGK PW NTHM NTK ZBPTD
YNGWK ZBET QKPTD ZEHFKJ
EQNXZ, ETJ ZBEZ PW TNZ QKPTD
ZEHFKJ EQNXZ.

6. H JHE NHE FX QHBBG CMYQ HEG CKJHE HU SKEO HU QX RKXU EKY SKZX QXA.

7. HBIHFOHTYH OV X TXUH HEHFQZTH COEHV MZ MWHOF UOVMXDHV.

8. QCO DLWK QCALH QCNQ MNL MDLJDWO DLO XDU ZOALH SDDU AJ OYQUNFNHNLMO.

9. JAQJV GZ SIBIA XQAI, NSH ANAIRU ZGCXRI.

10. WSNCA W XRRQ QZFFCA RFC OWF SRAXZHC WFMERQM, CHCF RFC'Y RJF ACDWNZHCY.

11. BFXDSQCU VCAXU VE DIYXUA PFCXQ OMQCUPG. MWPCQ M PXHC PFCE NKSAC PFCH. QMQCDE, XW CYCQ, SI PFCE WIQAXYC PFCH.

12. XGIJU CLSTUR CF DLRTRPTUS J IJU'R JMNJUELR JUM LUMR CF CHGEVTUS ATR DLPDLJP.

13. NTCBLX FW LRT KIZX LRFIY LRCL LFQT HCIIKL RCJQ.

14. NCWOT VOXVOJOTB BDO BVYLWXD CP WMBBOV CEOV WYTK, FLJB MJ WOT VOXVOJOTB BDO BVYLWXD CP WYTK CEOV WCVMSJ.

15. GH CJZ SJI'B FPB PNPMCBXGIF CJZ OEIB, BXGIA JH BXP BXGIFT CJZ SJI'B FPB BXEB CJZ SJI'B OEIB.

Answers on page 126.

Answers

Within each group, odd-numbered answers precede even-numbered ones.

Marcus Aurelius Antoninus ——————————

1. A good man makes no noise over a good deed, but passes on to another as a vine to bear grapes again in season.

3. Man must be arched and buttressed from within, else the temple will crumble to dust.

5. If not seemly, do it not; if not true, say it not.

7. Execute every act of your life as though it were your last.

9. Very little is needed to make a happy life.

11. Nothing befalls any man which he is not fitted to endure.

13. What is bad for the hive is bad for the bee.

15. Everything that exists is the seed of that which will come out of it.

2. All things from eternity are of like forms and come round in a circle.

4. It is not death that a man should fear, but he should fear never beginning to live.

6. The man who doesn't know what the universe is, doesn't know where he lives.

8. The present is the same for all; what we lose or win is just the flying moment.

10. Time is a river of passing events, a rushing torrent.

12. It is a shameful thing for the soul to faint in the race of life, while the body still perseveres.

14. The true worth of a man is to be measured by the objects he pursues.

Jane Austen ——————————————————

1. Business may bring money, but friendship hardly ever does.

3. Selfishness must always be forgiven, because there is no hope of a cure.

5. Vanity working on a weak head produces every sort of mischief.

7. An annuity is a very serious business.

9. People themselves alter so much that there is something new to be observed in them forever.

11. One cannot always be laughing at a man without now and then stumbling on something witty.

13. One half of the world cannot understand the pleasures of the other.

15. One man's way may be as good as another's, but we all like our own best.

2. How quick come the reasons for approving what we like!

4. It is very difficult for the prosperous to be humble.

6. In nine cases out of ten, a woman had better show more affection than she feels.

8. It is truth universally acknowledged that a single man in possession of a good fortune must be in want of a wife.

10. A narrow income has a tendency to contract the mind and sour the temper.

12. Those who do not complain are never pitied.

14. A lady's imagination is very rapid; it jumps from admiration to love, from love to matrimony in a moment.

Francis Bacon

1. Nature is often hidden, sometimes overcome, seldom extinguished.

3. Hope is a good breakfast, but it is a bad supper.

5. The best part of beauty is that which a picture cannot express.

7. Fortune is like the market, where many times, if you can stay a little, the price will fall.

9. Man prefers to believe what he prefers to be true.

11. He that gives good advice builds with one hand; he that gives good counsel and example builds with both.

13. Anger makes dull men witty, but keeps them poor.

15. It is a miserable state of mind to have few things to desire and many things to fear.

2. He that will not apply new remedies must expect new evils.

4. No pleasure is comparable to standing upon the vantage-ground of truth.

6. Virtue is like a rich stone, best plain set.

8. The joys of parents are secret, and so are their griefs and fears.

10. There is in human nature generally more of the fool than of the wise.

12. The worst solitude is to have no real friendships.

14. Impatient people are like the bees; they kill themselves in stinging others.

Honoré de Balzac

1. It is easier to be a lover than a husband, for the same reason that it is more difficult to be witty every day than now and then.

3. All human power is a compound of time and patience.

5. All happiness depends on courage and work.

7. Life is a garment; when it is dirty, we must brush it; when it is ragged, it must be patched; but we keep it as long as we can.

9. Power is not revealed by striking hard or often, but by striking true.

11. Discouragement is of all ages: in youth it is a presentiment, in old age a remembrance.

13. A hobby is a happy medium between a passion and a monomania.

15. In love, nothing is as convincing as a bold folly.

2. Marriage often unites for life two people who scarcely know each other.

4. Nothing so fortifies a friendship as a belief on the part of one friend that he is superior to the other.

6. Little minds find satisfaction for their feeling, good or bad, in little things.

8. Love is to the moral nature exactly what the sun is to the earth.

10. Every criminal is an atheist, though he doesn't always know it.

12. Vice is perhaps the desire to know everything.

14. Human passions are quite as strongly agitated by small interests as by great ones.

James Matthew Barrie

1. It is not true that woman was made from man's rib; she was really made from his funny bone.

3. Never ascribe to an opponent motives meaner than your own.

5. I have always found that the man whose second thoughts are good is worth watching.

7. They that have had romance have slipped in and out of heaven.

9. We never understand how little we need in this world until we know the loss of it.

11. To die would be an awfully big adventure.

13. Genius is an infinite love of taking pains.

15. Comfort is grand and you cannot expect to be both grand and comfortable.

2. God gave us our memories so that we might have roses in December.

4. If it's heaven for climate, it's hell for company.

6. Nothing is really work unless you would rather be doing something else.

8. Those who bring sunshine to the lives of others cannot keep it from themselves.

10. Every man who is high up loves to think he has done it all himself; and the wife smiles and lets it go at that.

12. Envy is the most corroding of the vices, and also the greatest power in any land.

14. Only where the heart is can the treasure be found.

Ambrose Bierce

1. What is worth doing is worth the trouble of asking somebody to do it.

3. Liberty is one of imagination's most precious possessions.

5. Women would be more charming if one could fall into her arms without falling into her hands.

7. Think twice before you speak to a friend in need.

9. To be positive is to be mistaken at the top of one's voice.

11. The gambling known as business looks with austere disfavor upon the business known as gambling.

13. Calamities are of two kinds: misfortune to ourselves, and good fortune to others.

15. If you would be accounted great by your contemporaries, be not too much greater than they.

2. Admiration is our polite recognition of another's resemblance to ourselves.

4. Take not God's name in vain; select a time when it will have effect.

6. A saint is a dead sinner, revised and edited.

8. The mouth in man is the gateway to the soul; in woman, the outlet of the heart.

10. A bore is a person who talks when you wish him to listen.

12. Beauty is the power by which a woman charms a lover and terrifies a husband.

14. You are not permitted to kill a woman who has wronged you, but nothing forbids you to reflect that she is growing older every minute.

Samuel Butler

1. To live is like to love: all reason is against it, and all healthy instinct for it.

3. Vices, like beasts, are fond of none but those that feed them.

5. The course of true anything never does run smooth.

7. Life is the art of drawing sufficient conclusions from insufficient premises.

9. The best liar is he who makes the smallest amount of lying go the longest way.

11. The one serious conviction that a man should have is that nothing is to be taken too seriously.

13. All the animals except man know that the principal business of life is to enjoy it.

15. Words are the clothes that thoughts wear—only the clothes.

2. Any fool can tell the truth, but it requires a man of some sense to know how to lie well.

4. Man is the only animal that laughs and has a state legislature.

6. Life is like playing a violin in public and learning the instrument as one goes on.

8. An empty house is like a stray dog or a body from which life has departed.

10. The public do not know enough to be experts yet know enough to decide between them.

12. Silence is not always tact, and it is tact that is golden, not silence.

14. You can do very little with faith, but you can do nothing without it.

Joseph Conrad ——————————————————————————

1. The mind of man is capable of anything because everything is in it, all the past as well as all the futures.

3. An ideal is often but a flaming vision of reality.

5. Any fool can carry on, but only the wise man knows how to shorten the sail.

7. Being a woman is a terribly difficult trade, since it consists principally of dealing with men.

9. Let a fool be made serviceable according to his folly.

11. The belief in a supernatural source of evil is not necessary; men alone are quite capable of every wickedness.

13. Nothing lays itself open to the charge of exaggeration more than the language of naked truth.

15. The real significance of crime is in its being a breach of faith with the community of mankind.

2. Woe to the man whose heart has not learned while young to hope, to love, and to put its trust in life!

4. Gossip is what no one claims to like, but everybody enjoys.

6. You shall judge of a man by his foes as well as by his friends.

8. The power of sound has always been greater than the power of sense.

10. To have his path made clear for him is the aspiration of every human being in our beclouded and tempestuous existence.

12. In plucking the fruit of memory one runs the risk of spoiling its bloom.

14. We live, as we dream—alone.

Daniel Defoe

1. Nature has left this tincture in the blood, that all men would be tyrants if they could.

3. All the good things of the world are no further good to us than as they are of use.

5. The only thing certain in life is death and taxes.

7. Self-destruction is the effect of cowardice in the highest extreme.

9. Wherever God erects a house of prayer, the devil always builds a chapel there.

11. He that has truth on his side is a fool as well as a coward if he is afraid to own it because of other men's opinions.

13. Wise men affirm it is the English way never to grumble till they come to pay.

15. In trouble to be troubled is to have your trouble doubled.

2. Fear of danger is ten thousand times more terrifying than danger itself.

4. Statesmen are always sick of one disease, and a good pension gives them present ease.

6. The best of men cannot suspend their fate; the good die early, and the bad die late.

8. Justice is always violent to the party offending, for every man is innocent in his own eyes.

10. All our discontents spring from the want of thankfulness for what we have.

12. A true-bred merchant is the best gentleman in the nation.

14. The height of human wisdom is to bring our tempers down to our circumstances.

Charles Dickens

1. If there were no bad people, there would be no good lawyers.

3. All of us have wonders hidden in our breasts, only needing circumstances to evoke them.

5. Rich folks may ride on camels, but it isn't so easy for them to see out of a needle's eye.

7. A man can never be a true gentleman in manner until he is a true gentleman at heart.

9. Dishonesty will stare honesty out of countenance any day of the week if there is anything to be got by it.

11. There is a wisdom of the head and a wisdom of the heart.

13. Every baby born into the world is a finer one than the last.

15. Take nothing on its looks; take everything on evidence.

2. Charity begins at home, and justice begins next door.

4. Never close your lips to those to whom you have opened your heart.

6. There are two styles of portrait painting: the serious and the smirk.

8. Money and goods are certainly the best of references.

10. The virtues of mothers shall occasionally be visited upon the children, as well as the sins of the fathers.

12. Every human creature is constituted to be that profound secret and mystery to every other.

14. A little learning is a dangerous thing, but a little patronage more so.

Benjamin Disraeli—————————————

1. Talk to a man about himself and he will listen for hours.

3. It is much easier to be critical than to be correct.

5. The youth of a nation are the trustees of posterity.

7. As a general rule, nobody has money who ought to have it.

9. Every production of genius must be the production of enthusiasm.

11. Time is precious, but truth is more precious than time.

13. The great secret of success in life is for a man to be ready when his opportunity comes.

15. The magic of first love is our ignorance that it can ever end.

2. A man who is not a liberal at sixteen has no heart; a man who is not a conservative at sixty has no head.

4. Next to knowing when to seize an opportunity, the most important thing in life is to know when to forgo an advantage.

6. Having the courage to live within one's means is respectability.

8. Nature has given us two ears but only one mouth, that we may hear from others twice as much as we speak.

10. My idea of an agreeable person is a person who agrees with me.

12. Every man has a right to be conceited until he is successful.

14. Increased means and increased leisure are the two civilizers of man.

George Eliot (Mary Ann Cross) ——————————

1. Animals are such agreeable friends; they ask no questions, they pass no criticisms.

3. The strongest principle of growth lies in human choice.

5. What loneliness is more lonely than distrust?

7. An ass may bray a good while before he shakes the stars down.

9. It is easy finding reasons why other folks should be patient.

11. Man clings because the being whom he loves is weak and needs him.

13. Keep true, never be ashamed of doing right; decide on what you think is right and stick to it.

15. The happiest women, like the happiest nations, have no history.

2. Truth has rough flavors if we bite it through.

4. A difference of taste in jokes is a great strain on the affections.

6. Anger and jealousy can no more bear to lose sight of their objects than love.

8. There is nothing that will kill a man so soon as having nobody to find fault with but himself.

10. To manage men, one ought to have a sharp mind and a velvet sheath.

12. The reward of one duty is the power to fulfill another.

14. It always remains true that if we had been greater, circumstances would have been less strong against us.

Ralph Waldo Emerson

1. Character gives splendor to youth and awe to wrinkled skin and gray hairs.

3. A true friend is somebody who can make us do what we can.

5. Nothing astonishes men so much as common sense and plain dealing.

7. A man must consider what a rich realm he abdicates when he becomes a conformist.

9. We are always getting ready to live, but never living.

11. Every man is an impossibility until he is born.

13. Men are all inventors sailing forth on a voyage of discovery.

15. Make the most of yourself, for that is all there is to you.

2. Use what language you will, you can never say anything but what you are.

4. If you would rule the world quietly, you must keep it amused.

6. The great majority of men are bundles of beginnings.

8. Whenever you are sincerely pleased, you are nourished.

10. Work and acquire and you have chained the wheel of chance.

12. Some thoughts always find us young and keep us so.

14. A friend is a person with whom I may be sincere.

Henry Fielding

1. Never trust the man who has reason to suspect that you know he has injured you.

3. Examples work more forcibly on the mind than precepts.

5. When I'm not thanked at all I'm thanked enough.

7. To whom nothing is given, of him can nothing be required.

9. Make money your God and it will plague you like the devil.

11. He that can heroically endure adversity will bear prosperity with equal greatness of soul.

13. It is a good maxim to trust a person entirely or not at all.

15. Money will say more in one moment than the most eloquent lovers can in years.

2. Love and scandal are the best sweeteners of tea.

4. Custom may lead a man into many errors, but it justifies none.

6. Money is the fruit of evil as often as the root of it.

8. Neither great poverty nor great riches will hear reason.

10. The prudence of the best heads is often defeated by the tenderness of the best of hearts.

12. What a silly fellow must he be who would do the devil's work for nothing.

14. When children are doing nothing, they are doing mischief.

Robert Frost

1. A man will sometimes devote all his life to the development of one part of his body—the wishbone.

3. In three words I can sum up everything I've learned about life: it goes on.

5. Americans are like a rich father who wishes he knew how to give his son the hardships that made him rich.

7. Take what is given, and make it over your way.

9. There are three great things in the world: there is religion, there is science, and there is gossip.

11. A jury consists of twelve persons chosen to decide who has the better lawyer.

13. By working faithfully eight hours a day, you may eventually get to be a boss and work twelve hours a day.

15. A liberal is a man too broadminded to take his own side in a quarrel.

2. Earth's the right place for love: I don't know where it's likely to go better.

4. Home is a place where, when you have to go there, they have to take you in.

6. Most of the change we think we see in life is due to truths being in and out of favor.

8. Education is hanging around until you've caught on.

10. The brain is a wonderful organ; it starts working the moment you get up in the morning and does not stop until you get into the office.

12. Families break up when people take hints you don't intend and miss hints you do intend.

14. A diplomat is a man who always remembers a woman's birthday but never remembers her age.

Kahlil Gibran

1. The truly great man is he who would master no one, and who would be mastered by none.

3. Every man is two men; one is awake in the darkness, the other asleep in the light.

5. Is not dread of thirst when your well is full the thirst that is unquenchable?

7. Generosity is giving more than you can; pride is taking less than you need.

9. The significance of man is not what he attains, but rather in what he longs to attain.

11. In much of your talking, thinking is half murdered.

13. When we turn to one another for counsel, we reduce the number of our enemies.

15. Ever has it been that love knows not its own depth until the hour of separation.

2. You give but little when you give of your possessions. It is when you give of yourself that you truly give.

4. Truth is a deep kindness that teaches us to be content in our everyday life and share with people the same happiness.

6. It is well to give when asked, but it is better to give unasked, through understanding.

8. You are the bows from which your children as living arrows are sent forth.

10. You cannot lay remorse upon the innocent nor lift it from the heart of the guilty.

12. Desire is half of life; indifference is half of death.

14. An exaggeration is a truth that has lost its temper.

Oliver Goldsmith

1. You can preach a better sermon with your life than with your lips.

3. If you were to make little fishes talk, they would talk like whales.

5. I love everything that's old—old friends, old times, old manners, old books, old wine.

7. Women and music should never be dated.

9. Wisdom makes but a slow defense against trouble, though at last a sure one.

11. Where wealth and freedom reign, contentment fails.

13. When I am determined, I always listen to reason because it can then do no harm.

15. The hours we pass with happy prospects in view are more pleasing than those crowded with fruition.

2. Lawyers are always more ready to get a man into troubles than out of them.

4. Age that lessens the enjoyment of life increases our desire of living.

6. The virtue which requires to be ever guarded is scarcely worth the sentinel.

8. We take greater pains to persuade others that we are happy than in endeavoring to be so ourselves.

10. The true use of speech is not so much to express our wants as to conceal them.

12. Friendship is a disinterested commerce between equals; love, an abject intercourse between tyrants and slaves.

14. People seldom improve when they have no other model but themselves to copy after.

Nathaniel Hawthorne ——————————————

1. Time flies over us but leaves its shadow behind.

3. Happiness in this world, when it comes, comes incidentally.

5. Every individual has a place to fill in the world and is important, in some respect, whether he chooses to be so or not.

7. A woman's chastity consists, like an onion, of a series of coats.

9. Selfishness is one of the qualities apt to inspire love.

11. Mankind are earthen jugs with spirits in them.

13. There is no such thing in man's nature as a settled and full resolve either for good or evil, except at the very moment of execution.

15. The best of us being unfit to die, what an inexpressible absurdity to put the worst to death.

2. A man's soul may be buried and perish under a dungheap or in a furrow of the field, just as well as under a pile of money.

4. Echo is the voice of a reflection in the mirror.

6. If a man were sure of living forever here, he would not care about his offspring.

8. What we call real estate, the solid ground to build a house on, is the broad foundation on which nearly all the guilt of this world rests.

10. The only sensible ends of literature are first, the pleasurable toil of writing; second, the gratification of one's family and friends; and lastly, the solid cash.

12. What is the voice of song, when the world lacks the ear of taste?

14. Labor is the curse of the world, and nobody can meddle with it without becoming proportionately brutified.

William Hazlitt

1. Wit is the salt of conversation, not the food.

3. The more we do, the more we can do; the busier we are, the more leisure we have.

5. Seek to gain the good will of others rather than to extort their applause.

7. Prejudice is never easy unless it can pass itself off for reason.

9. Everyone in a crowd has the power to throw dirt; nine out of ten have the inclination.

11. The love of liberty is the love of others; the love of power is the love of ourselves.

13. He who undervalues himself is justly undervalued by others.

15. We are not satisfied to be right unless we can prove others to be quite wrong.

2. Those who can command themselves, command others.

4. When a thing ceases to be a subject of controversy, it ceases to be a subject of interest.

6. The art of pleasing consists in being pleased.

8. The art of life is to know how to enjoy a little and to endure much.

10. We never do anything well until we cease to think about the manner of doing it.

12. The most silent people are generally those who think most highly of themselves.

14. We may be willing to tell a story twice, never to hear it more than once.

Aldous Henry Huxley

1. Great is truth, but still greater, from a practical point of view, is silence about truth.

3. Facts do not cease to exist because they are ignored.

5. Experience is not what happens to you; it is what you do with what happens to you.

7. To his dog, every man is Napoleon; hence the constant popularity of dogs.

9. Actual happiness always looks pretty squalid in comparison with the overcompensation for misery.

11. There are few who would not rather be taken in adultery than in provincialism.

13. There is something curiously boring about somebody else's happiness.

15. The pleasures of ignorance are as great, in their way, as the pleasures of knowledge.

2. The only completely consistent people are the dead.

4. Those who believe that they are exclusively in the right are generally those who achieve something.

6. Happiness is like coke—something you get as a by-product in the process of making something else.

8. Most human beings have an almost infinite capacity for taking things for granted.

10. The silent bear no witness against themselves.

12. Drink with impunity, or anyone who happens to invite you!

14. Several excuses are always less convincing than one.

Samuel Johnson

1. The natural flights of the human mind are not from pleasure to pleasure, but from hope to hope.

3. Marriage has many pains, but celibacy has no pleasures.

5. There must always be a struggle between a father and a son; while one aims at power, the other at independence.

7. Labor's face is wrinkled with the wind and swarthy with the sun.

9. Such is the state of life that none are happy but by the anticipation of change.

11. It is better to suffer wrong than to do it, and happier to be sometimes cheated than not to trust.

13. Life is a pill which none of us can bear to swallow without gilding.

15. To improve the golden moments of opportunity and catch the good that is within our reach is the great art of living.

2. No man ever yet became great by imitation.

4. Wickedness is always easier than virtue, for it takes the short-cut to everything.

6. Criticism is a study by which men grow important and formidable at very small expense.

8. Money and time are the heaviest burdens of life, and the unhappiest of all mortals are those who have more of either than they know how to use.

10. Nothing can be truly great which is not right.

12. He who waits to do a great deal of good at once will never do anything.

14. Love is the wisdom of the fool and the folly of the wise.

Rudyard Kipling

1. All the people like us are we, and everyone else is they.

3. The silliest woman can manage a clever man; but it needs a very clever woman to manage a fool.

5. Gardens are not made by singing "oh how beautiful" and sitting in the shade.

7. He travels the fastest who travels alone.

9. Some women will stay in a man's memory if they once walked down a street.

11. No one thinks of winter when the grass is green.

13. Daughter am I in my mother's house, but mistress in my own.

15. A woman is only a woman, but a good cigar is a smoke.

2. Borrow trouble for yourself if that's your nature, but don't lend it to your neighbors.

4. Words are the most powerful drug used by mankind.

6. Being kissed by a man who didn't wax his mustache is like eating an egg without salt.

8. You can never tell when you've opened a hell, how soon you can put back the lid.

10. A woman's guess is much more accurate than a man's certainty.

12. Men speak the truth as they understand it, and women as they think men would like to understand it.

14. If you want to win your battles, take and work your bloomin' guns.

Henry Wadsworth Longfellow

1. Great is the art of beginning, but greater the art of ending.

3. It is difficult to know at what moment love begins; it is less difficult to know that it has begun.

5. Sorrow and silence are strong, and patient endurance is godlike.

7. Thy fate is the common fate of all; into each life some rain must fall.

9. Three silences there are: the first of speech, the second of desire, the third of thought.

11. All your strength is in union. All your danger is in discord.

13. Still achieving, still pursuing, learn to labor and to wait.

15. The heights by great men reached and kept, were not attained by sudden flight, but they while their companions slept, were toiling upward in the night.

2. Most people would succeed in small things, if they were not troubled with great ambitions.

4. In this world a man must either be anvil or hammer.

6. The everyday cares and duties, which men call drudgery, are the weights and counterpoises of the clock of time.

8. Let him not boast who puts his armor on as he who puts it off, the battle done.

10. Some must follow and some command, though all are made of clay.

12. Do not delay; the golden moments fly.

14. In character, in manner, in style, in all things, the supreme excellence is simplicity.

W. Somerset Maugham

1. Money is like a sixth sense without which you cannot make a complete use of the other five.

3. At a dinner party one should eat wisely but not too well, and talk well but not too wisely.

5. Life is so largely controlled by chance that its conduct can be but a perpetual improvisation.

7. People will sometimes forgive you the good you have done them, but seldom the harm they have done you.

9. Sentimentality is only sentiment that rubs you up the wrong way.

11. People ask you for criticism, but they only want praise.

13. It is salutary to train oneself to be no more affected by censure than by praise.

15. American women expect to find in their husbands a perfection that English women only hope to find in their butlers.

2. Sincerity in society is like an iron girder in a house of cards.

4. The value of culture is its effect on character.

6. To acquire the habit of reading is to construct for yourself a refuge from almost all the miseries of life.

8. Marriage is a very good thing, but I think it's a mistake to make a habit of it.

10. There is only one thing about which I am certain, and this is that there is very little about which one can be certain.

12. Common sense and good nature will do a lot to make the pilgrimage of life not too difficult.

14. The soul is a troublesome possession, and when man developed it he lost the Garden of Eden.

Ogden Nash

1. We go through life pulling on doors marked push.

3. A family is a unit composed not only of children but of man, woman, an occasional animal, and the common cold.

5. Life is not having been told that the man has just waxed the floor.

7. There is only one way to achieve happiness on this terrestrial ball, and that is to have a clear conscience, or none at all.

9. Marriage is the alliance of two people, one of whom never remembers birthdays and the other never forgets them.

11. People who work sitting down get paid more than people who work standing up.

13. Why did the Lord give us so much quickness of movement unless it was to avoid responsibility.

15. Middle age is when you have met so many people that every new person you meet reminds you of someone else and usually is.

2. Progress might have been all right once, but it's gone on too long.

4. In real life it only takes one to make a quarrel.

6. Life is stepping down a step or sitting in a chair, and it isn't there.

8. To keep your marriage brimming with love in the loving cup, whenever you're wrong admit it, whenever you're right, shut up.

10. If you want to get the most out of life, why the thing to do it is to be a gossiper by day, and a gossipee by night.

12. Parents were invented to make children happy by giving them something to ignore.

14. The people who think they can wind up ahead of the races are everybody who has ever won a bet.

Dorothy Parker

1. Wit has truth in it; wisecracking is simply calisthenics with words.

3. Where's the man that could ease a heart like a satin gown?

5. It's not the tragedies that kill us, it's the messes.

7. By the time you swear you're his, shivering and sighing, and he vows his passion is infinite, undying—lady, make a note of this: one of you is lying.

9. Every love's the love before in a duller dress.

11. Travel, trouble, music, art, a kiss, a frock, a rhyme—I never said they feed my heart, but still they pass the time.

13. Most good women that are hidden treasures are only safe because nobody looks for them.

15. Four be the things I'd been better without: love, curiosity, freckles, and doubt.

2. Four be the things I am wiser to know: idleness, sorrow, a friend, and a foe.

4. The best way to keep children home is to make the home atmosphere pleasant, and let the air out of the tires.

6. People who do things exceed my endurance; God, for a man that solicits insurance.

8. The two most beautiful words in the English language are "check enclosed."

10. You can't teach an old dogma new tricks.

12. People ought to be one of two things: young or dead.

14. Better to be left by twenty dears than lie in a loveless bed.

William Shakespeare

1. He that wants money, means, and content is without three good things.

3. Unbidden guests are often most welcome when they are gone.

5. Modest doubt is called the beacon of the wise.

7. To climb steep hills requires a slow pace at first.

9. Love sought is good, but given unsought is better.

11. The web of our life is of a mingled yarn, good and ill together.

13. Nothing can seem foul to those that win.

15. It is not strange that desire should so many years outlive performance.

2. We know what we are, but know not what we may be.

4. Men's evil manners live in brass; their virtues we write in water.

6. Things without all remedy should be without regard: what's done is done.

8. Everyone can master a grief but he that has it.

10. The silence often of pure innocence persuades when speaking fails.

12. There lives within the very flame of love a kind of wick or snuff that will abate it.

14. The better part of valor is discretion.

George Bernard Shaw

1. Marriage is popular because it combines the maximum of temptation with the maximum of opportunity.

3. There are two tragedies in life. One is not to get your heart's desire, the other is to get it.

5. A man's star is not complete without a woman's garter.

7. If pity is akin to love, gratitude is akin to the other thing.

9. A perpetual holiday is a good working definition of hell.

11. First love is only a little foolishness and a lot of curiosity.

13. The people who get on in this world are the people who get up and look for the circumstances they want.

15. It is dangerous to be sincere unless you are also stupid.

2. A man never tells you anything until you contradict him.

4. There is no love sincerer than the love of food.

6. A living failure is better than a dead masterpiece.

8. Self-sacrifice enables us to sacrifice other people without blushing.

10. What really flatters a man is that you think him worth flattering.

12. Man can climb to the highest summits, but he cannot dwell there long.

14. Hatred is the coward's revenge for being intimidated.

Robert Louis Stevenson

1. To be idle requires a strong sense of personal identity.

3. Keep your fears to yourself but share your courage.

5. The price we pay for money is paid in liberty.

7. Some strand of our own misdoing is involved in every quarrel.

9. Man is a creature who lives not upon bread alone, but principally by catchwords.

11. To travel hopefully is a better thing than to arrive.

13. A great part of life consists in contemplating what we cannot cure.

15. In every part and corner of our life, to lose oneself is to be the gainer; to forget oneself is to be happy.

2. The most beautiful adventures are not those we go to seek.

4. The cruelest lies are often told in silence.

6. Politics is perhaps the only profession for which no preparation is thought necessary.

8. There is no duty we so much underrate as the duty of being happy.

10. Books are good enough in their own way, but they are a mighty bloodless substitute for life.

12. Everyone lives by selling something.

14. A certain sort of talent is indispensable for people who would spend years together and not bore themselves to death.

Jonathan Swift

1. Every man desires to live long, but no man would be old.

3. There are few wild beasts more to be dreaded than a talking man having nothing to say.

5. It is useless for us to attempt to reason a man out of a thing he has never been reasoned into.

7. A wise man is never less alone than when he is alone.

9. Happiness is the perpetual possession of being well deceived.

11. Whoever makes the fewest persons uneasy is the best bred in the company.

13. When a true genius appears in the world you may know him by this sign: the dunces are all in confederacy against him.

15. There is nothing in this world constant, but inconstancy.

2. Punning is a talent which no man affects to despise but he that is without it.

4. No man will take counsel, but every man will take money; therefore, money is better than counsel.

6. Complaint is the largest tribute heaven receives and the sincerest part of our devotion.

8. Some people take more care to hide their wisdom than their folly.

10. Old sciences are unraveled like old stockings, by beginning at the foot.

12. The stoical scheme of supplying our wants by lopping off our desires is like cutting off our feet when we want shoes.

14. It is with wits as with razors, which are never so apt to cut those they are employed on as when they have lost their edge.

Henry David Thoreau

1. A man is rich in proportion to the number of things which he can afford to let alone.

3. Some circumstantial evidence is very strong, as when you find a trout in the milk.

5. One may almost doubt if the wisest man has learned anything of absolute value by living.

7. He enjoys true leisure who has time to improve his soul's estate.

9. It is the marriage of the soul with nature that makes the intellect fruitful and gives birth to imagination.

11. It is the man determines what is said, not the words.

13. A man cannot be said to succeed in this life who does not satisfy one friend.

15. Books are the treasured wealth of the world, the fit inheritance of generations and nations.

2. We cannot do without our sins; they are the highway of our virtue.

4. It takes two to speak truth—one to speak and another to hear.

6. One man lies in his words and gets a bad reputation; another in his manners and enjoys a good one.

8. One cannot too soon forget his errors and misdemeanors; for to dwell upon them is to add to the offense.

10. Make the most of your regrets; to regret deeply is to live afresh.

12. It is an interesting question how far men would retain their relative rank if they were divested of their clothes.

14. A sky without clouds is a meadow without flowers, a sea without sails.

Mark Twain (Samuel L. Clemens)————————

1. Soap and education are not as sudden as a massacre, but they are more deadly in the long run.

3. One of the most striking differences between a cat and a lie is that a cat has only nine lives.

5. Necessity is the mother of taking chances.

7. The compliment that helps us on our way is not the one that is shut up in the mind, but the one that is spoken out.

9. It usually takes more than three weeks to prepare a good impromptu speech.

11. Each person is born to one possession which outvalues all the others—his last breath.

13. Thunder is good, thunder is impressive, but it is the lightning that does the work.

15. Every man has a secret ambition: to outsmart horses, fish and women.

2. Few things are harder to put up with than the annoyance of a good example.

4. Nothing so needs reforming as other people's habits.

6. The man who does not read good books has no advantage over the man who can't read them.

8. When one has broken the tenth commandment, the others are not of much account.

10. Man is the only animal that blushes, or needs to.

12. Get your facts first, and then you can distort them as much as you please.

14. Often, the surest way to convey misinformation is to tell the strict truth.

Oscar Wilde

1. It is absurd to divide people into good and bad. People are either charming or tedious.

3. Duty is what one expects from others.

5. There is only one thing worse than being talked about, and that is not being talked about.

7. Experience is a name everyone gives to their mistakes.

9. Truth is never pure, and rarely simple.

11. Children begin by loving their parents. After a time they judge them. Rarely, if ever, do they forgive them.

13. Beauty is the only thing that time cannot harm.

15. If you don't get everything you want, think of the things you don't get that you don't want.

2. A little sincerity is a dangerous thing, and a great deal of it is absolutely fatal.

4. When we blame ourselves, we feel no one else has a right to blame us.

6. A man can be happy with any woman as long as he does not love her.

8. The only thing that can console one for being poor is extravagance.

10. After a good dinner one can forgive anybody, even one's own relatives.

12. Woman begins by resisting a man's advances and ends by blocking his retreat.

14. Women represent the triumph of matter over mind, just as men represent the triumph of mind over morals.

Index

acceptance, 117, 118, 122, 124
actions/deeds, 106, 109, 117, 121, 122
adaptation, 114
admiration, 109
adultery, 118
advice, 107
aging, 106, 107, 109, 113, 116, 121, 124
agreeableness, 112
ambition, 125
Americans, 114, 120
anger, 107, 113
animals, 112, 113
annuity, 106
Antoninus, Marcus Aurelius, 106
approval, 107
aspirations, 110
attention, 121
Austen, Jane, 106–107
babies, 112
Bacon, Francis, 107
bad, 106
Balzac, Honoré de, 107–108
Barrie, James Matthew, 108–109
beauty, 107, 109, 126
beginning/ending, 119
Bierce, Ambrose, 109
blame, 126
blushing, 126
books, 117, 123, 125
bores, 109
business, 106
Butler, Samuel, 109–110
celibacy, 118
certainty, 120
chances, 125
change, 106
character, 121
characters, 113
charity, 112
chastity, 116
checks, 122

children, 112, 114, 116, 121, 122, 126
choice, 112
churches, 111
Clemens, Samuel L., 125–126
cleverness, 119
clothing, 125
clouds, 125
comfort, 108
common sense, 121
complaints, 107, 124
compliments, 125
conformists, 113
Conrad, Joseph, 110–111
conservatives, 112
consistency, 118, 124
contemplation, 123
contentment, 116, 122
contradiction, 123
controversy, 117
conversation. See talk/conversation
counseling, 107, 115, 124
courage, 108, 111, 112, 122, 123
crime/criminals, 108, 110
criticism, 112, 118, 120
Cross, Mary Ann, 112–113
crowds, 117
culture, 120
curiosity, 122
customs, 114
danger, 120
daughters, 119
death, 108, 111, 113, 115, 116, 121, 122
Defoe, Daniel, 111
desire, 107, 119, 124, 125
destiny, 106
determination, 116
Dickens, Charles, 111–112
diplomats, 115

disasters, 109, 123
discontent, 111
discouragement, 108
discretion, 122
dishonesty, 111
Disraeli, Benjamin, 112
distortion, 126
distrust, 113
dogma, 122
dogs, 118
doubt, 122, 124
drinking, 118
drudgery, 120
duty, 123, 126
echoes, 116
education, 115, 125
Eliot, George, 112–113
Emerson, Ralph Waldo, 113
emotional support, 121
endurance, 119
enemies, 122
English women, 120
envy, 109, 125
evidence, 112, 124
evil, 110, 114, 116, 118, 119, 122
exaggeration, 115
examples, 125
excuses, 118
expectations, 118
experience, 117, 126
experts, 110
facts, 117, 126
failure, 123
faith, 110
families, 115, 121
fate, 106, 119
fathers, 118
fear, 106, 107, 123
feelings/emotions, 109, 114. See also specific emotions
Fielding, Henry, 114
fish, 115

flattery, 123
followers, 120
food, 123, 126
fools/foolishness, 107, 110, 111, 119
forgiveness, 120, 122
freckles, 122
friendship, 106, 107, 108, 109, 113, 116, 122, 125
Frost, Robert, 114–115
gambling, 109, 121
gardens, 119
generosity, 115
genius, 108, 112, 124
Gibran, Kahlil, 115
gifts, 114, 115
God, 114
Goldsmith, Oliver, 115–116
good/goodness, 106, 111, 116, 119, 126
gossip, 110, 114, 121, 126
gratitude, 123
greatness, 109, 118, 120
grief, 122
guests, 108, 122
guilt, 115
habits, 125
happiness, 106, 108, 113, 116, 118, 121, 123, 124, 126
hatred, 123
Hawthorne, Nathaniel, 116–117
Hazlitt, William, 117
heartache, 121
hobbies, 108
holiday, 123
home, 110, 114, 122
honesty. See truth/honesty
hope, 107, 114, 116, 118